Solomon & George Publishers
414 South Gay Street
Auburn, AL 36830

1. Literature (general). 2. The South.

ISBN 978-0-9853404-0-7

First Edition

10 9 8 7 6 5 4 3 2 1

# Mission of Solomon & George Publishers

Solomon & George Publishers is a division of Gnu Arts Inc., a 501(c)(3) non-profit organization located in Auburn, Alabama. Gnu Arts is dedicated to promoting and fostering the arts in all genres: literary, visual, and performing. As a non-profit press, Solomon & George (S&G) Publishers has a mission of publishing work by new and established writers speaking to and preserving the life and culture of the South, and reprinting currently unavailable work important to our history as a people.

The name of the press, Solomon & George, is a tribute to two extrodinary women writers from Alabama: Olivia Solomon and Anne George. Both women made lasting contributions to the world in many ways, not the least of which was through their writing. Some of each writer's work is included in this inaugural publication to introduce new readers to them and to remind the rest of us of the talent lost when these women departed our midst.

And now you are invited to read, react, and remember.

*To: Doug & David*
*Two of my favorite Southern Gentlemen!*
*Always,*
*Andrew Tidwell*

# Chinaberries & Crows:
# An Anthology

### Bert Hitchcock, Editor

S&G
SOLOMON
AND GEORGE
PUBLISHERS

# Table of Contents

# SECTION III
## Remembering

# SECTION IV

# SECTION V

# Introduction

When to write this introduction I had to think once more about the differences of geographical place, I started my consideration abstractly. Immediately, though, two specific personal experiences jumped to mind.

The first was international. Several decades ago I almost worked out a faculty exchange with an American literature scholar at a university in northern England. The exchange was to be an academic-year long, and we were to swap homes as well as faculty positions. The discussion went well until the two of us began to get down to details, in particular the facts of public transportation. To make a sad story short, the public touting of Auburn as a lovely "village" brought to a British mind (and that of a non-motor vehicle driver) something other than the American reality. Partly because of trains—or rather the absence of passenger train service here—as well as (at that time) the situation for more local non-automobile transportation, our negotiations quickly became derailed. I can still hear, in all its Englishness: "But I thought Auburn was a village."

Geographical, political-boundary differences? Varying social and cultural histories here, correct?

The second, very brief, more recent occurrence had to do with regional differences in the U.S. For anyone exiting the Atlanta airport terminal into a hellishly hot Georgia afternoon after having walked out into snowy 20-degree temperature in Wyoming that morning, there is no intellectual issue of any kind involved. There is simply visceral knowledge, pure topological and climatic fact.

These latter scientific conditions, of course, greatly *affect* if not basically *effect* human life and culture, wherever. East central Alabama is different from scores of other global places. And here, even within this limited area, when certain social, political, and economic elements figure in, Auburn can be seen to be distinctively different from Opelika, and Opelika from rural Lee County. The following statement only splits hairs perhaps, but saying it makes me more comfortable somehow, and might just help ward off a little regional jingoism: Let us acknowledge it is not finally actual physical location but the human beings thereof that we are dealing with when we (scholars and non-scholars both) wax on about "place."

Thinking about a certain place will likely move the thinker pretty quickly into the more philosophical territory of time. Places, and especially the human occupations there (I don't mean just jobs), do change over time. (Climates do, too, most of us now think—but over longer periods?) Stereotypes, based essentially on a contemporary distinctiveness if not uniqueness (but often not really wide commonality across a region), get formed at certain historical points. They then hang on, and sometimes on, and on, and on.

Although I laugh—a lot sometimes—at their jokes and agree with some of their scholarship, I don't have much patience with professional Southerners, individuals who for profit and fame traffic in the character stereotypes for this region. Focusing too much on superficial differences makes them lose sight both of superficial similarities and, basic human commonalities, it seems to me. Such obsession keeps us all, whether primary or secondary purveyors or consumers, excessively limited and bound by time past.

Not long ago an Alabamian I know had occasion to observe that rather than the old stereotypic romantic emblems of moonlight, mockingbirds, and magnolias, a more realistically accurate, widely appropriate iconic descriptive trio for the United States South would be (1) blinding, blistering summer heat, (2) crows, and (3) chinaberry trees. The observation proved to be suggestive for this present anthology and is evident in its title. But the contents of the volume were never intended to be limited to those narrow examples of birds and botany. The intent or hope, rather, was to gather writing that recounted or grew out of direct experience in a real, small particular geographical part of the world. Theoretically, technically—the idea or ideal might be stated—the writing connected in various ways with this locale would be genuine and organic, emerging from and formed by what seemed to have actually been or to have transpired. Pre-existing concepts or prefabricated forms would not have been imposed upon the creative process, and therefore not upon a final literary product.

Since I am not one of the selected writers included, I can say without any encumbrance of conscience that I think this objective has been achieved. As was believed from the outset, limiting contributors to persons with ties to the Auburn-Opelika, Alabama, area meant little qualitative restriction at all. Just in case you didn't know it before, the collection you now hold provides more than sufficient evidence that we have had and do have a bounty of good writers "right cheer."

The pages that follow offer a great deal of literary variety—and I choose the closing adjectives and nouns of my preceding clause very deliberately. Poetry, fiction, non-fiction (essay, memoir…)……we need not get tied up in genre labels. We can just read and be affected, enjoy and ponder, conclude and question, be informed and be moved. Though not chosen or ordered on any basis of chronological time, personal or otherwise, selections here deal with childhood and adolescence, with young and middle and old adulthood, and with death. Unlike the larger human life experience, however, in experiencing this volume we can proceed straight through OR just dip in and out however we wish.

Wherever our physical location the progression of time does, of course, carry us ultimately, literally to matters of life and death—and, right now, to an explanation. The eulogies concluding this collection are not usual for an anthology of this kind. The passing of four fine writers with varying Auburn associations during the months the volume was being prepared could not and did not fail to be felt deeply by their East Alabama friends and admirers. Some among the latter wrote memorable memorial tributes that were offered publicly if transiently at the time. Their words, we thought, deserved to be given new life in somewhat more enduring form.

Let me end with birth. To have been a small part of the inaugural publication of S & G Publishers has been more than a small pleasure and honor. Now it's time for you to join me, with commensurate satisfactions and benefits, in the premiere. It is readers, of course, who in fact create a premiere. I believe we will all soon be saying:

"Bon voyage."

And, and then, "And many more."


Bert Hitchcock
Auburn, Alabama
Spring, 2012

# SECTION I
Anne Carroll George & Olivia Solomon

# Autumn Apples

## by Anne Carroll George

We hiked to Turkey Creek,
taking a shortcut
through woods that glowed
golden in the sun. On rocks
over the falls, we ate apples,
throwing cores into the water,
laughing as our lips touched.
Then we lay on leaves
that crackled as we
moved together rhythmically.

Now that I sleep
encased in an aging body
strange how you
dominate my dreams—
eighteen—
your tongue tasting of apples.

# The Grist Mill
## by Anne Carroll George

Afternoon sun pours over us.
We say only it is a beautiful day
but neither of us would be surprised
if maple leaves drifting to the creek
stayed suspended, small tongues of flame
against blue layered sky.
The mill wheel creaks and turns.
Water leaks from the trough,
pools over smooth sandstone.
The path, too, is smooth,
ochre with iron ore.

A sign almost hidden by chokeberry
and goldenrod says John Wesley Hall
built this mill, 1860, operated it
sixty years. Surely, I think,
there was a day like this for him
with butterflies and blackeyed Susans
when he sat by his dam and watched deer
across the creek and thought he
would never die, that under such a sky
death was impossible. And when wrapping
the day around him like a patchwork quilt
he waded, as we do now, into the stream,
feeling the water, patient, cool
close around his feet.

# Josie-in-the-morning
## by Anne Carroll George

The water oaks talk among
themselves. They brush me
with tendrils of Spanish moss,
whisper who are you, why
are you here. I hear them
over the rasp of the roof
rusting in the nearby swamp.
It is that kind of day.

Josie-in-the-morning, your
house is gone. Here are the
double front steps curving
toward nothing; snakes sun
on the hearth. They stretch,
say yes, the place has changed.
No pretense to perfection.

Half awake, I hear kindling
spark, hear Josie measuring
corn. Slugabed, look,
God is ironing the field.
Golden shadows push through
the hay. Nervous chickens
caw Josie, Josie! She
throws them corn, brings
me a handful of sunshine
still green, she says,
but it will ripen.

# My Grandmother's Story

## by Anne Carroll George

Try living with someone sixty years, child,
there'll be more missing than a finger.
That's no lie.
And him saying, "Oh, Alice, I'm bleeding to  death,"
staggering around like a stuck pig.
And me saying, "You are not,"
which of course he wasn't,
and going to fetch the coal oil.
But, you know, that man still blames me,
says I ruined his handwriting, of all things.
A plain lie.
Three-fourths of the blood was from the chicken
which nobody even noticed was still flopping around
and which the old fool should have held tighter.

I'll tell you this, though, about his finger.
When he quit pointing, things got better.

# Quilting

by Anne Carroll George

We sit at the frame
three women backstitching,
eight stitches to an inch
the way our grandmother
taught us. Alternating
triangles of "Heaven and Earth"
reflect and shadow afternoon sun
and the radio plays softly as we
talk about the yellow material
from Alice's skirt and how it looks
next to the dark blue with roses.

Soon we will straighten fingers
just beginning to gnarl,
stretch our backs and go home
to fix supper for the husbands
we married thirty years ago

But not for a while.

The sun gathers golden
in my sister's parlor and
dust motes sparkle in the
slanting light. Dishwashers,
grown children, and darkness
seem far away. We
place triangles together
as we have done so often
and stitch, thimbles blinking
lights across the pattern.

# Turned Funny

## By Anne Caroll George

Southern women turn funny sometimes
when what the creek don't drown
the locust eat up or the sun comes up
wrong side of the house. Good women,
turned funny, like my aunt Alma who,
leaving a pot of beans to burn,
did a mean cancan out in the yard
flipping her skirt over white cotton drawers
that nearly blinded a couple of truckers.

And Southern families hold up their heads
straight as a church choir on Sunday.
"When Mama turned funny," they say proudly,
"she dived from the banisters, smashed
the zinnias." Or "Judy sends postcards to Jesus."
And now my family, God bless them, chime in.
"Our Anne," they boast, "she writes poetry."

# The Prophetess
## by Olivia Solomon

THE FIRST vision came to her when she was twelve years old. She always slept on the outside of the bed, her younger sisters towards the wall. So it was no trouble to get up when the old woman appeared at the hearth. The fire should have been out, but it was bright and fresh, and by its light she could see the figure clothed in a dark garment, the only visible flesh, a withered face, rutted like a naked gully, a sharp chin, the mouth shriveled, sucked in, the broad nose curving as an ingrown toenail almost to the lip, the eyes bold in their hollowed sockets, black and shining, and the twisted hands stretched out in greeting. The figure spoke soft and clear: *Come.* She rose without effort or hesitation, in perfect obedience.... The crippled hands smoothed her long hair, free from its tight daytime plaits. The woman bent to place her dried lips on her cheek.

Through winter darkness the child followed, neither curious nor afraid, but when they reached the well she wondered why she was not cold, why her bare feet did not feel the frost. The figure lowered the bucket into the well. The chain did not squeak, nor did the bucket swing to and fro at the beginning of its descent. She did not hear it hit the water, but she watched the chain wind itself up soundlessly as it ascended. The figure reached for the bucket, full to the rim, but no water sloshed over the side, took the dipper from a nail, dipped, and offered it to the girl. She drank, remembering that it was forbidden, for her mother had drawn up a dead rat from the well yesterday. The taste was sweet and pure but it did not satisfy, and a great thirst overcame her. She must quench it or die. She began to dip furiously, but a twisted hand lightly intervened. The tormenting burn in her belly suddenly ceased.

"Eat." The girl took a small piece of bread from the out stretched crippled hand. Immediately, as with the water, a great hunger came to her. The answer came, "Nay." And the fierce stab for food was gone. The black figure led her away towards the woodpile, neatly divided into stacks of kindling, stovewood, and logs, the axe blade stuck clean into one of the logs. "Kneel," and she obeyed. "I have brought you the gift. You cannot forsake it nor can it leave you. You shall keep it all the days of your life." The girl felt new, as if something had been poured into her, filling the secret insides, stretching her bones so that her limbs seemed to be growing before her very eyes. And as she marvelled, the dark figure vanished. Her mother was shivering at the back door when the girl reached the porch.

"Suzannah?"

"Yes, ma'am."

"What on earth do you mean out here in the backyard in the middle of the night? Barefoot. In the dead of winter. Lord only knows you'll take the pneumonia."

"I came to get a drink of water, mama." Her mother clutched the child's icy body, led her to the front room where she and her husband slept in an iron bedstead, the baby between them. She snatched a quilt from the bed, wrapped the girl in it, shook her husband awake.

"Get up, build a fire, quick, build a fire." He was up instantly, busy with the fire. The mother sat in the rocker near the fire, holding the stiff, quilt-draped child. After a time when the fire was going good, she said, "Found her out in the backyard, barefoot, said she was going after a drink of water, drinking out of the well when she knowed good and well a rat had died in it. There was a plenty fresh water in the kitchen, child. My Lord, my Lord." The child's face was pale and vacant. Her flesh quivered, her bones began to shake violently. She thrashed out of her mother's lap, and fell to the hearth.

"Hold her, hold her, for God's sake, she's having a fit, get her tongue. Hush, hush up child, you'll wake the baby. Lord, what's the matter with her?"

The girl clawed her face and screamed tearlessly. *Ahh, eeeeeeee, ahhhhh, eeeeeeee.* Her legs flew in the air and her mother tried to pull her nightgown down. One arm jerked loose and fell into the fire. Together the mother and father dragged the child off the hearth. She fought them, and they fought back, pinned her down, the mother holding her legs, the father her head and arms. All her motion stopped, she opened her eyes wide and said, her voice quavering near tears, "My arm burns." They released her, and all the taut strength of her bone and flesh collapsed. Her father picked her up and laid her in the bed, murmuring comfort. "Now, now, it's gone be all right, it's gone to be all right, it's gone to be all right. Just wait and see. Now, now." He smoothed lard grease on the burn, then covered her to the shoulders. For a time she made no sound, the tears ran down her cheeks onto the pillow. They stood above, her mother smoothing her hair and forehead, brushing the tears away. The child grabbed her mother's hand.

"I don't know why I went with her mama, she was old and ugly, she had on something black, and her hands was all twisted up, but she told me to drink the water, and she gave me some bread to eat, and it was like I couldn't not do it, had

14

to do it, but I wasn't ascared of her. Not then I wasn't. Something woke me up and she was just standing there by the hearth and she motioned me to go with her, and I went and when we got to the well, she let down the bucket and drawed it up and give me some from the dipper, and then she give me some bread and I eat it, and then she took me to the woodpile and told me she had brought me a gift, but she didn't hand me nothing that time, just said she had a gift and I couldn't never forsake it and it couldn't never leave me. And I felt funny all over, and she went away, and then I was afraid. Oh, mama, I'm so afraid. Papa, papa, will I die?"

When she went to sleep, her mother and father sat by the fire for the rest of the night, watching her, pondering over what they had seen, waiting for morning. At daybreak she was still asleep. The baby woke, the mother gave him her breast. She made breakfast for her other children, helped the older ones dress, and sent them to school. The father went to the fields. Noon came. The child did not wake until mid afternoon, woke to see her mother nursing the baby at the fire.

"I been asleep a long time, ain't I, mama?"

"You was tired and sick, girl, so I let you sleep. You feeling better?"

"Yes, ma'am, but I'm sore all over, like I fell down. What made me sick, mama?"

"You just had a little seizure in the night, something like a fever, but it's passed over now. You think you could eat a bit? Some cornmeal gruel? I made you some."

"I ain't hungry."

"Well, you got to eat to live, whether you want to or not."

"Did I wake the baby?"

"The Devil hisself couldn't wake him up. You watch him now while I go get your gruel." The mother fed the girl spoonful by spoonful until she had eaten half the gruel.

"Mama, how'd I get burned? And why come I got all these bruises and scratches on me? I don't remember none of it."

"I told you, Suzannah, you had a little seizure. You'll be all right tomorrow. And you had a bad dream about an old woman and you wandered out to the well with her, and you caught a cold out there barefoot." Her voice carried a mother's authority and assurance. The child was convinced, but the mother was troubled in her heart. Suzannah was her second child, the first having been born maimed and deformed, dying within a week, so this was the eldest living, and not for a single day since she was born had she ever been uneasy about her, not until now.

The child mended within the week. For months they watched her carefully and just as their fears were laid, the second vision came. This time she came to their bed at night.

"Get up, mama. Something's happened to Uncle Will. He's at the back door amoaning, crumpled up, his shirt is all tore up and he's ableeding and some of his teeth is out, somebody's beat him up and stabbed him. Come on, be quick, papa."

The mother never doubted the child for an instant. But there was nobody at the back door.

"I seen him, I just now come out here and seen him, mama, I know I did. He's crawled out in the yard somewhere. I'll find him."

They searched the yard, stopped, listened for sounds. The spring air was sweet. Finally, the father turned her to him, his big hands gripping her shoulders so hard her bones burned.

"Suzannah, you lied. There ain't nobody out here, wasn't ever nobody out here, not brother Will or anybody else. I'm gone whip you, child, I'm gone whip you for lying. Lying is a sin before God, and no child of mine is gone tell a lie as long as I live and draw breath."

She did not plead to be released from the whipping, or beg him to believe her, or appeal to her mother. She only said "Papa, I didn't tell no lie." And somehow he knew she was not lying, but he had to whip her, because there was no bloody man moaning and crawling around at the back door, and that was the truth his eyes and ears told him, that was what had to go on. He bent her slim form over a sawhorse, took his pocketknife and cut off a switch; not many times had he whipped his children, and then only the boys, never a daughter. He stripped it of its leaves, and he began. The keen wood drew blood on her legs the first time.

His wife cried "No, don't do it, no, for God's sake!" But when she understood that he had to and would, even though he didn't want to, she turned her back to it, leaning against the side of the smokehouse, her head boring into the gray, smooth boards. She heard the early morning bird noises, the slap of the switch, over and over.

At last the mother forced herself to look. Her daughter's body curved inwards with every stroke, but she made no sound; her husband's arm curved again and again, moving upwards from the legs to the thighs, the buttocks, across her back. When he thrust the switch from him, the rooster crowed. The child tumbled to the ground, her head and arms across the sawhorse. The man wiped sweat from his face with his sleeve and walked to the back porch where he took water from

16

the bucket, poured it into a tin pan and washed his face. She led her daughter into the house, bathed her wounds, changed her gown, and laid her in bed to sleep.

At noon a boy Suzannah's own age, her cousin, brother Will's son, came to tell them his papa was bad off, was dying. Had come fifteen miles in a mule and a wagon to tell them how his mother found his daddy bloody, moaning, at the back door, beat up, stabbed, came to tell them what they already knew. Suzannah's father rose from his meal, early green beans and corn bread and onion, reached for his cap, and harnessed his mule. His wife, carrying the new baby on her hip, stood beside the wagon, and said, "I don't reckon the child lied."

"I knew she wasn't lying."

When his brother lay buried in the hole he himself had helped dig, in the coffin he had helped make, in the clothes he had put on him, he came to his daughter's bedside and knelt to her. Her hands caressed his head as he wept. It was clear that the girl had the gift of prophecy and that she must be heeded. But she was young and tender, flesh of their flesh, and her visions and dreams would be kept secret so that she would not be badgered and mocked.

A good girl, obedient and dutiful at household tasks, working in the fields during hard times and abundant seasons, feeding hogs and chickens, watchful over her younger brothers and sisters, conscientious in her studies, they rarely heard her laugh or saw her romp and play. Her voice was sweet and high, but she sang only in church. She grew into womanhood beautiful, but wore no ornaments, chose only the simplest clothes, did not so much as wear a ribbon or a lace. She was much at her sewing for her younger sisters and at her embroidery. Every bed in the house was covered with sheets and pillowcases she had embroidered, cool and fresh. All living things bloomed at her touch and even among the dirt of her flowers she appeared extraordinarily clean. The neighbors remarked on her industry and kindness, she's got the makings of a good wife, a good mother. Yet they sensed her strangeness, the difference in her, the feeling that she was waiting for a nameless thing, that she was already in the service of a great mission, belonged to it, body and soul, accepted it with the peculiar grace that comes from the acceptance of inevitability, pledged to it with the serenity of those in religious orders. They had heard vaguely she was subject to fits, the possessor of secret knowledge, some envious ones believed it, others dismissed it. It was hard to believe of a girl so lovely and clean and good.

Sometimes she did not prophesy for months. Then she grew anguished, hoping that the gift had left her forever, knowing for a certainty that it would come again.

As the days in June stretch out blue, then build up clouds until a wild storm sheds abroad death and damnation, so did the seizure come. Or again, there would be many small, sharp seizures following hard upon one another, pinpricks that increased in depth and intensity until she was exhausted. Both ways there was agony which she concealed from her parents, went off by herself as a dog goes off to be sick or die, keeping the final secrets to herself, returning to them spent, the message distilled, reduced, clear. Afterwards, she would sleep for a long time, and when her vision was fulfilled, sometimes at the very moment of happening, sometimes a week or a month later, she again went about her life, to flowers and sewing, went in peace.

Once, when they were all off in a far field, she went apart from them for awhile into the woods. Her mother and father laid down their hoes when they saw her coming, ready for her bidding. She told them the barn was on fire, and when they caught sight of it, the roof was collapsing. Again, one evening as they sat by the kerosene lamp in the quiet minutes before bedtime, she ceased her sewing, stiffened in her chair, closed her eyes tightly as if against the noonday sun, rose with haste, like one who suddenly sick blindly seeks a place to vomit. But the seizure had come too quick, she did not make it outside, only to her room. She managed to close the door, but they heard her agony. Thuds and thumps as she rolled on the floor, sounds that did not resemble even those of an animal, garbled, strangely foreign words, screams *ahhhh, eeee*, like those she made the night when the black figure appeared to her. It went on for an hour or more. The father sat with his head in his hands, nearly between his knees, the mother crooning, rocking back and forth, holding her stomach as if in the early hours of childbirth. The questions of the younger children were silenced. One of them snickered and his father slapped him across the face. After that, they all sat rigid as their father and mother mourned the pain of their daughter, lamented as if she were already dead. When she came back to them, her face clawed, her hair flowing down her back, she told them, her voice but every word pronounced separately, where to go and what they would see, every horrible detail gone over and not a rag of pity fluttering near, death and destruction recited as a child might his prayers or lessons. The mother and father comforted their younger children, who now knew their sister as a prophetess, piecing together the odd bits of behavior that had floated by them over past years, their minds flickering back and forth, teasing their discovery as they might a small animal or insect which they tortured to death. Though cautioned to silence and secrecy, they needed no threats from their father. They would be afraid of their sister until the day they died.

And Suzannah's mother and father came to the place of the murder, a house like their own, five miles away, a house shaded with oak and pecan trees, with chicken yard and barn and hogpen and garden and fields, a house which sheltered a man and his wife and their children. Two little boys, lying in bed, quilts up to their chins, dead by strangulation. A girl of perhaps nine or ten years slain in the hallway. The eldest son, his arms and legs lopped off, soaking in blood on the kitchen floor. And the father, sitting on the steps of the front porch, an axe beside him, cradling his mutilated wife. And in his madness he invited them in for supper.

The time came when Suzannah would be married. They gave her fearfully to the man, a carpenter who wooed her with song and accordion, who sometimes came courting in the middle of the day, his rule in his back pocket, his hammer slung from his hips, his apron full of nails, doing his best to tease her into laughter, throwing her up in the air and catching her, carrying on any sort of foolishness. And when she did laugh, her mother and father caught their breaths, stopped their hearts, praying that when her husband took her, the gift would forsake her, that this man would fill her with children, transform her entirely to wife and mother. If not, he would know soon enough what they knew. There was no need to tell him.

And for a time if seemed as if the carpenter would succeed. Her father gave them a few acres of land for a house and garden and cow, and in the months before the marriage, Suzannah went with Jesse and watched him build their house, watched him clear the ground, lay the foundations, saw and nail and plane the new yellow boards, and she began to feel that he, too, was the possessor of a mystery; he went about his work with total absorption and sureness. Yet he was merry, ever ready for a frolic with her brothers or a neighbor, good naturedly leaving off his work to wrestle or go fishing. She could not help but smile at his jokes and games. When the house was finished and they brought in their furniture, a bed and mattress from her mother, chairs and tables from his mother, they celebrated their marriage.

She knew long before the monthly blood stopped that she was going to have a child, and for nine months she had no seizures, no visions. He was foolish in his attention and affection, shy in talking about the baby. She was taken on a cold night, sent him for her mother, lay in the bed alone until they came back. He waited in the kitchen, lamps lit all over the house, fires burning. When her mother told him it would not be long, she saw that he was crying. He asked "Why don't she scream? Why don't she holler? I can't bear it, her in there hurting, and not screaming." She thought she should tell him there and then that his wife had known pain far greater than this, ought to tell him about the fits, time he knew of his wife's gift. But she didn't. She just said Suzannah never did take on much when she was sick.

When her mother laid the baby in Suzannah's arms, skinny and gray, still and quiet, she turned her face to the wall. The child, a girl whom its grandmother had to name, for its mother would do nothing but dispassionately tend and nurse it, sickened in its third month. It did not ever cry, sometimes it made little mewing noises, nor did it seem to sleep much, but lay in its cradle and stared, appearing to hold in its deep blue eyes secrets which it would not speak, even if it had tongue. They sent for a doctor, twenty miles away, but he told them nothing nor gave them hope.

The first time Suzannah willingly picked up the baby was the morning of its death. She stood over its crib, heard its hard breathing, saw the blue face, lifted it to her breast and held it until the last breath went out of it. Then she bathed its gray body, tiny and shrunken, terribly old, clothed it in a snow white gown, laid it in its cradle with fresh linen, sat in the rocking chair beside it until her mother came and saw the dead child.

"You turned from her, Suzannah, from her the minute she was born. God forgive you, unnatural woman not to love your own child. Go down on your knees, girl. Go down on your knees to God Almighty." Suzannah wailed the long cry for the dead, wept for her shrunken gray child, for whom her breasts were still swollen, whose infant mouth was now stiff and aged.

"My God, my God, mama, mama, don't you know why I turned from her, Oh my sweet Jesus, ain't nobody never loved nothing like I loved her, oh my precious baby, oh lord in Heaven, Oh God, nobody'll ever know how I prayed for her to live, oh mama, I saw her dead, saw her sicken, saw me dress her in this dress, before she was ever born. Mama, I don't want to be able to see things, I have asked God and asked God to take it away, mama, I want to die, I'd rather be dead with this child than to have to go through it again."

Jesse found the two women sitting on the side of the bed, their arms about each other. But not until nearly a year later, after the birth of their first son, did he know his wife was a prophetess. One day when he came home at noon there was no dinner, the door to their bedroom was closed. His wife lay on the floor unconscious. The baby slept in the crib. He thought some assailant had ravished and beaten his wife.

But she woke and without rising from the floor she said clearly with long pauses between her words, "Jesse, your mama is dead. She's laying in the backyard, her

eyes wide open. Chickens are apecking at her face. Go, Jesse, and raise her up."
He thought she had gone mad. Nothing could convince him that she had not been
beaten into madness. He lifted her to the bed, bathed her clawed face, kissed her,
and begged her to tell him who had done this awful thing to her. The man that did
it would not live to see the sun go down. But she would say nothing. He could not
even rouse her to tend the baby. She collapsed into sleep. But Jesse's mama was
dead, and when she was buried, Suzannah told him of the gift of prophecy that
came on her first when she was twelve years old. But the soul of the carpenter,
merry and gay, could not believe her, though he well knew that there were strange
things in the world, that giants had once walked the earth, that the Holy Bible told
of bones dancing and fiery wheels, of burning bushes and Lazarus raised from
the dead. He would see to it that, even if she had once prophesied, she would
prophesy no more; he would match his love against the forces which possessed
her, nothing on earth or in heaven, he swore, would so ravish his wife while he yet
lived. And for a while he made his oath good.

Two more children were born to them, sons, a year apart. For four years,
while the babes grew, loved and watched over, his wife had no visions. They were
about her always as she kept the house, tended garden, cow, and chickens. Jesse's
carpentry prospered. He built house after house and with the money he bought
land, furniture, put in lights and running water, purchased a Ford automobile,
bought it without ever learning how to drive it, nor thinking to ask anybody how
to, just getting in it and howling and singing, the two boys solemn with wonder,
his wife holding on to the seat, chickens and dogs fleeing, the very trees and
bushes leaping back at its advance, and not knowing how to stop the thing, drove
on and on until it gave out of gas and jiggled to a stop.

In the eighth month of another pregnancy, Suzannah waked one night
moaning. So long had it been that at first Jesse thought her time had come. But it
was the long ritual of her seizure, the descent of power which she battled until it
conquered and she lay still, brought into supreme clarity. Jesse tied her limbs to
the bed, but she broke her bonds. Her mouth began to move. Quickly he clasped
his hands over it. He would still the voice; she would not speak what she had seen.
If she did not speak it, it would not come to be. She did not struggle; her eyes were
closed; he could feel her lips moving against his palms. By God, he would break
her jaw, tear out her tongue. He would stop the words; if there was no word, there
would be no death.

He rose the next morning and the next, waiting to see if the prophecy would be fulfilled. Often he would find her at night on her knees by the boy's bed, praying. Once he heard her pray, "No, God, no, oh God, no, spare them," and the soul of the carpenter trembled. The fourth child was born, another son, and still whatever she had seen had not come to pass.

This last child was of unnatural strength and quickness. At one month he would leap from her arms, and nursed as if he would never get enough. At seven months he was walking, stumbling over his little gown, falling off the high front porch, emerging with perhaps one bump and a grin. At a year, he was swinging the cat by her tail, wandering off into high grass and weeds, dumping milk out of the pail over his head, banging his fingers with his father's hammer. She was after him always.

The two older boys were angelic. They smiled on the baby's antics, stroked him when he was sleeping or nursing. But they kept to themselves, behaving almost like twins, playing quietly under the house, looking for doodlebugs, building frog houses around their feet, sitting for long spells in the water oak shade, beside their mother carrying stovewood or gathering pears and figs. To the mother, the young one was like a fly she had to swat away again and again or a cow that kept kicking at milking time, no matter how she tried to soothe it, or a butterfly she pursued in vain. She could not keep him clean as she could the other two; his mouth was always smeared, his hands grimy, his feet dusty or caked with mud. He wiggled and skidded away and hid under the blanket when she tried to change his diapers. He would fall asleep suddenly, lie like one dead until morning, and then begin his antics all over again. He was his father's delight, and even his mother, after trying a thousand ways of correction, surrendered to his joy. A constant irritant, he was yet beautiful and warm, hugging and kissing her wetly. But the two elder boys gave her peace and goodness, lying with their arms about each other at night. It was those two she prayed for.

Because they were frail, she was quick to notice the slightest change in them, so at the very onset of the disease she shuddered, though Jesse assured her the fever and sore throat were due to the coming of cold weather. In the first few nights of their sickness, she rose time and again to feel their foreheads, to give them water, to bathe and change their nightclothes, sing to them until they slept again. As it worsened, she rubbed them with turpentine and lard, keeping the fire in their room all night, letting them out of bed during the day for only a little while to play before the hearth or in the sunshine of the front porch. At her urging Jesse brought the doctor who gave them cough syrup, aspirin, a black ointment, and chucked them under their chins. They would be well in a few days.

But Suzannah knew exactly how many days they would be ill. Every day, every minute she watched her unspoken prophecy fulfill itself. She cared for them in a dream with the feeling of having already done this or that thing exactly in this manner. She did not have to look in their throats to see the membrane forming over the tonsil, spreading to the soft palate, the voice box transforming itself from the slimy raw egg white to a tough, rubbery brownish red, winding itself like a parasitic vine, finally enveloping as kudzu covers a whole clay bank then passes on to devour trees and bushes, cleverly green in summer, dying deviously in winter leaving gray serpentine fields. Daily their pallor increased, their noses ran, whatever they ate they vomited. Their smell was unbearable; often she opened the windows, but the rush of cold air did not kill the odor. Jesse again brought the doctor, though Suzannah did not ask for him. After he had touched them gently, he stood on the front porch gazing over the spring fields as he told them flatly diptheria was killing their sons. Harsh, abrupt, he confessed that he had no medicines to heal, muttering something about the Great Physician.

And now Suzannah's eyes followed the curve of the fields. A sweet wind bearing the earth's fresh green blew her hair across her face, brown silken strands across her lips and eyes. Lightly she pulled the floss away and tucked it behind her ears, her gesture so serene and lovely that it broke Jesse's heart, and he clenched his fist and beat the wall, his back hunched in sorrow and rage. Tearless, she thanked the doctor, and the man wondered for a moment if she suffered shock. But her hand was cool and soft, her deep blue eyes clear and kind. Long ago she had wept for her sons, and so she turned to keep watch until death came, to sit up night after night, to walk softly day after day about their beds.

She observed every detail with remoteness, knowing exactly when a certain symptom would appear. She heard their lovely low voices become a nasal whine, saw strong tea come back through their noses, the peculiar eye squint. Sometimes they smiled crookedly. They would say "I'm sorry, Mama" when they soiled themselves and the bedclothes, turning not to her but to each other, their arms about each other in sleep. They knew they would die and they told her so. She did not disavow their knowledge.

In his prosperity Jesse had bought a Morris chair and he had marvelled at the ingenuity of the thing, how he could take the slender steel rod and adjust it so that the chair had three positions, from upright to reclining to flatness. The day came when Suzannah saw her sons choke to death. The five year old died first, she held him in her arms until his face turned black, carried him to the parlor, with one hand let down the Morris chair and laid him there. She returned to hold the younger one, to sing to him as he struggled to breathe, holding him first against her shoulder as she might an infant, then against her breast, rocking and smoothing his cheeks until he too was black and still. Then she carried him and laid him beside his brother, two small skeletons, their long gold hair flowing over the green velvet of the Morris chair. Then she summoned Jesse, who wept for his sons and took up his hammer and saw and nails and built two small coffins.

When Jesse and Suzannah brought their sons to the church for burial, the community marked her faith and quiet. She watched the dirt fall on two small boxes, shushed her youngest and only son, smiled at him, returned to the Ford automobile and went home. That night Jesse beat her until his strength wore out. She had killed his sons, not God, but their own mother. She did not cry out or try to shield herself from the beating. Some deep, queer thing warned him not to kill her and he retreated as if before a forbidden, holy altar, though at the last, she begged him to do it, to release her from the hell of her prophecies.

Suzannah bore one more son, a serious scholarly child who did well in school. These two brothers were also bound together as if they were two orphan brothers, for their mother was stern and remote, careful to see to their needs, but never close to them. After they passed two years she did not take them on her lap or wind their arms about her neck. She taught them their prayers, directed the memorization of Scripture, and was strict with their studies. Their father was rarely in the house; he was in his fields with his hands or away directing other men who built houses for him. When his boys were old enough he took them with him and taught them his crafts, and both were charmed with building and cultivating the earth, one grave, the other mirthful. Their father was silent when he was near their mother, husband and wife said only what was needful but when he was away with his sons, often he burst into song, and sometimes he pulled long and hard from a bottle of whiskey he always kept about him. Once or twice, drunk, he brought his accordion into the parlor, sat in the Morris chair, and played and sang half the night, but his wife did not complain.

When the son of laughter was twelve, his younger brother brought him bleeding and unconscious to Suzannah; she had clearly seen her son mount the forbidden horse, clutch the black animal about its neck, yell and grin as rider and horse reared up on its hind legs; had seen the downward thrust, another mighty rearing up and the rider flash towards the sun; heard the sound of the body hitting the earth and hooves trampling soft flesh. She saw her younger son throwing stones and screaming at the horse until the animal fled, saw him lift his brother, the right leg dangling and bloody. And so she saw her sons coming from afar off, left her work, wounded son in her arms, carried him to her bed, ripped away his clothing, and bathed the mangled limb.

At the hospital the doctor ordered immediate amputation, but Suzannah would not consent. He tried to prevail upon her, warning that the flesh would rot and the boy die, but still she did not consent. Her boy would walk on earth crippled, but he would not die. Her queer assurance maddened the doctor. The boy lay there two weeks passing sieges of great fevers, the wounds festering and foul, his mind coming and going from death to life. At the end of the third week he walked from the hospital, pulling hard on the shoulders of his father and brother.

The limb grew crooked and shorter than the other so that until the day he died he limped slightly, every step a hard pain. The flesh shriveled, blackened, sometimes it flamed up, raw and running with pus. Then he would go apart from the others, late at night to his mother, who stripped off the proud flesh, raked away the putrefaction, soothed the limb with ointments and bandaged it. No being ever saw the wound save his mother, not even his father, or his brother who loved him.

Again and again Suzannah saw her son of mirth wounded, near death, beaten in honky-tonks, where he danced and drank and took after strange women. Once she saw him knifed in the back at a cockfight, watched as he whirled around to his assailant and struck as a serpent, then walked steadily to the pit, claimed his spurred cock, and drove off, blood spilling onto the car seat. Each time he came home wounded to her, she showed no surprise, gave him no admonishment, but bathed him and healed him. And each time her anguish preceded his, her soul devoured with foreknowledge of his wounds.

Both sons loved the automobiles Jesse bought them, sleek and shiny things they polished and pored over, crawled under and into, familiar with every intricate twist of the engines, whining and moaning under their touch. On Sundays she no longer asked them to church, for they worked on their cars all God's morning, then in the long Sabbath afternoons whirled up dust devils along the country roads or plunged through creeks, the water above the running boards. Often they came home walking, leaving the car hopeless in mud. Not once did the serious son wreck his car; he drove just within the limit of daring, and when he carried a girl with him, he even drove sedately, kindly. But the wild son went far beyond daring, and his automobile was often smashed and battered.

25

The older son racked from dance hall to honky-tonk, from bootlegger to moonshiner, but the younger was much at home with his books. Patient and methodical, he went through four years of Latin, translating lessons for his brother, two grades ahead, who used the language well enough for obscene jokes and parodies that outraged the teacher. As the younger son went deeper into his books, his love for the land diminished. Yet it tortured him to see his brother sow his fields carelessly and reap abundance while he labored for a scant harvest. In anguish he observed his crippled brother maneuver over roof tops lithe as a cat, his hammer plunging a nail into wood with two blows, laying brick after brick brilliantly as if he handled only air. Jealously, he saw his brother caress his cattle into milk and meat, his pastures into rich green, full of new calves, while he bungled his own portions. But he could not forsake his books; the line from print to eye began to extend to all his being, to pull him away from earth and her weathers.

At last with grace he conceded those victories to his crippled brother whom he now came to admire and to love above all men. On the day of his graduation from high school he announced that he would pursue the law, thereby separating himself forever from his people. For seven years he sought the law, returning home only at Christmas, which was no longer kept in the house except for the feast, his mother warning that he was leaving God, that he sought the wrong law; returned once a year to the hard blow on the shoulder, which signified his brother's love, to his father's befuddlement that his son would abandon field and wood and home for books. The only other time he came home, his crippled brother lay dying. It was after this that his mother changed.

In all the years since the gift of prophecy had come to her, Suzannah had not endured such pain as with the vision of her crippled son spinning violently in his automobile as it plunged down the steep ravine. Bits of shattered glass and twisted metal pierced her body. Her screams were the screams of her maimed son, flung through the windshield into snaky vines and thorns. For a long time she lay as he lay, twisted and shuddering, her face and hands bleeding, then as one dead by the road. She rose up and told Jesse where they must go. Long had he ceased doubting her prophecies and he took her to the white bed where his favorite son lay.

Suzannah had seen him dead, had seen the coffin lid close over his face. The doctor said he was sorry, there was nothing he could do, but his mother said he shall not die, he shall live. She shut the door against the doctor and her husband and entered the presence of death. And she covenanted with God for the life of her son, "Spare him and I shall no longer rage against the gift. Give him to me, Oh God, who hast come down to me in fire and blood, who hast scourged me with death and pain. Spare my son, fulfill not this prophecy, and I shall not deny Thee. I will cry aloud, spare not my voice. I will lead Thy people, I will speak Thee to them, so that they shall not remain comfortless. Let my son rise, take up his bed and walk, and I shall teach men to do justly, love mercy, and walk humbly before Thee. Let him come forth as Lazarus, and I shall cast bread upon the waters. Let him rise up as eagles and not faint, let his chastisement be upon me, and I shall go into the waste places and declare the glory of the Lord. Require not my son as a living sacrifice, and I shall tell men of weeping and wailing and gnashing of teeth and of the Holy City, Jerusalem, prepared as a bride adorned for her husband." And the angel of the Lord descended to Suzannah's dead son and blew into him the breath of life.

After the covenant, power descended softly. Suzannah had only to close her eyes, and it would come. She invited it, begged for its coming. In supplication she bowed to it. It enveloped her with unbearable sweetness. Nor did she keep her gift secret. Seekers came by day and by night; to them she spoke not only of the approach of death and sickness but of births, harvests, marriages. It was spread abroad that she could heal the blind, the deformed, the diseased, but she gently denied such knowledge promising only to intercede with the blessed Jesus. Many times she rose in church to speak with tongues, not rolling on the floor and clawing her face, but holding up her arms to heaven and crying low in a garbled language. When the Spirit released her, all her old body shrank. With her head bowed she translated for the congregation what the tongues had said. She told them of hard times to come, of men killing for bread, of children dying with the swollen bellies of starvation. And finally she began to bring sinners to the mourner's bench, to pray with them for forgiveness of sin, to go with them to baptism, where their vile and filthy bodies were washed in the water which was the blood of the Lamb. All went in fear and awe of her, save her sons who were ashamed. And Jesse as well acknowledged her as the prophetess of God.

One by one Suzannah prophesied the deaths of her parents, her brothers, her sisters. When she stood beside the open grave of her last brother, she vowed she would go no more to a burying. Not long after she herself was brought near death's door. And when God gave back her life, she swore that water would never touch her head again. Her hair was long and thick, never once cut in her life, and she would wash the feet of Jesus with her tears and dry them with her hair.

She dreamed the long illness and death of her husband before it came. In his sickness he loved her as he had in his youth. Since her own illness, a shaking had come over her. Her head made incessant small tremors. Her skin grew slack, her eyes were filming over with the cataracts that would ultimately take her sight. But she soothed his parched body with her shaking hands, bent her trembling head over his pillow, bathed even his male parts which in all their marriage she had never seen until now. She sat beside him night and day, drawing his pain into her, until finally she heard, as he slept, the death rattle in his throat. She committed his soul to the death angel, bathed his body for the last time, kept watch over it in the first bought coffin that ever entered her house, but did not follow it to its last resting place. When the sons of Jesse came home, having carried the coffin between them into the church and out again and watched it lowered into the grave, they found their mother at work in her flowers. Her sons took wives; the son of mirth a frail, spindly creature who worshipped him, whom he abused with his debaucheries; the serious son a plump chatterbox who liked card games and flowered hats. The serious son explained to his wife that his mother was the harmless victim of religious hysteria, of mild hallucinations. The son of mirth said his mother was crazy. The serious son told his mother of Muhammed, Buddha, and other strange gods, patiently seeking to unseat her faith, but she answered the fool hath said in his heart there is no God. The son of mirth laughed at hell, and she answered every knee shall bow and every tongue shall confess. To both of them she said it is a fearful thing to fall into the hands of a living God. Yet she blessed her sons, for the one had suffered greatly and the other had pitied his brother's suffering with all his heart.

The sons tripled their father Jesse's fortune and gave Suzannah grandchildren, the son of mirth two daughters, the serious son, three sons. And in the instant of their first breath the prophetess foresaw all the days of their lives, hearing in their first scream the sound of their dying. And her grandchildren grew unto her, about her, in her last blind days they did not leave her. Though her prophecies were strange to them, they held themselves open to her truth and they did not mock her. She saw their fathers die, the grave son cut off as he spoke in a house where the laws of men are written; and she mourned for him, for the suddenness of his going, and prayed that he be remembered for his graces, that he be not far from the bosom of Abraham, and she saw that her petition was freely granted for she had kept the covenant. The son of mirth suffered a long time, and in his suffering confessed the name of Christ, sent for the elders of the church to anoint his head with oil, and besought the prophetess to pray for his life, but she would not.

When he saw that he would surely die, he begged her for the promise of salvation, which she gave in gentleness and which he took in peace.

Suzannah's last great vision came in her ninetieth year. In the house of God, she lifted up her eyes, the sockets matted, the eyeballs bloody, and saw pestilence and war and hunger and death, great cities melted, millions of bodies writhing like maggots, emaciated thousands, naked, piled into enormous ditches, children poisoned, infants tossed on spikes, their limbs ripped off before their mother's very eyes. In her blindness she saw Armageddon. Then she rendered up her soul and saw the face of God.

# Section II
## Contributors

# Coming of Age
## by Mary Belk

It was almost dawn when Molly Ames turned over on the lumpy mattress of her brass bed and reached for her flannel housecoat. The bitter chill in the air was uncommon in South Alabama, and her cold, chapped hand shivered as she switched on the light. The sudden glare lit up her sparsely furnished room. On the dresser, beside Molly's worn Bible, was a picture of her husband in his Navy uniform. It was the last photograph taken of him before he was killed in action. Molly wondered why she kept the snapshot. Her impression of him was renewed each time she looked at her teenage son, Joey.

Molly passed her son's room as she started toward the kitchen. She tapped lightly on the door, then pushed it open. "Joey," she called. Except for his head, he was completely buried under a mountain of quilts. "Get up. We've got boarders coming today." She hesitated before adding, "the circus people."

Molly turned and crossed the hall. She went into the kitchen, an oversized room with high ceilings and shelves lined with homemade pickles and preserves. She hoped Joey had remembered to bring in the wood for the stove. Molly found the stove empty. She rushed down the back steps to the woodpile and returned to the kitchen, her trembling arms filled with firewood.

Molly started a fire in the tin stove and set a kettle of water on to boil. She stayed close to the fire, letting her chilled body soak in the glow of warmth. She was a slight, middle-aged woman with soft sorrowful eyes. She wore her graying hair pulled back from her face in a bun.

Molly heard the clock strike six as she took the bacon from the frying pan, poured off the excess grease, and started to spoon thick pancake batter onto the griddle.

Joey bounded into the kitchen. "Morning, Ma." He looked freshly scrubbed, and his wavy, black hair was parted neatly on one side. His dark eyes sparkled.

"Good morning, Joey." She set a plateful of pancakes and bacon in front of him. "You're mighty cheerful."

"The circus is coming!" He smiled, pouring a stream of fig syrup on the hot buttered griddlecakes. "I've got to hurry if I want to get to Benson's pasture in time to watch them unload."

"There's ice on the ground, Joey. The circus might not stay with it so cold."

"Oh, Ma, bad weather won't stop the show." He stuffed a bite of bacon in his mouth. "And Ma, when the boarders get here, call me Joe."

"I will if I remember," she said. "But I'm not trying to impress any circus people. I wouldn't have them here at all if we didn't need the money." She wiped the countertop with a damp dishrag. "If this depression ever ends, I'll never have paying guests in my house again."

Joey gulped down a swallow of milk, shoved his plate back, and got up.

Molly followed him to the kitchen door. "Can you get a job helping set up the tent?"

"And miss all the excitement?" He sounded incredulous.

"We could use the money."

Joey shrugged. "I'll try." He was almost to the front door now.

"Joey!" Molly called after him. "Be sure you wear your coat and hat!"

"Yes, Ma," he answered impatiently.

"Joey?" She yelled again.

"Ma'am?"

"Try to bring home some respectable boarders. You know how...."

"Okay, Ma." He let the screen door slam, crossed the porch, and ran down the front steps two at a time.

As Molly watched him go, she wondered if this would be the time she would lose him. Whenever the circus came, she was afraid her son would leave with it. She knew she'd have to give him up sometime, but she didn't think she could stand losing him to the circus the way she had lost his father to the sea. But he was drawn to the circus in a way she couldn't understand, and he talked about the performers as if they were mysteriously enchanting. "Those folks are just plain working people," she pointed out. "The circus is a trade to them like any other job." But Joey would not be disillusioned.

Molly finished her hot coffee and began clearing the dishes from the table. This was not the time to worry about her son; she had to get ready for the roomers. Molly became so absorbed in her chores that she was startled several hours later when she heard her son's footsteps on the front stairs.

Joey appeared in the hall carrying two cardboard suitcases held together with rope. "Ma, they're coming. They're right behind me," he said breathlessly. "Is everything ready?"

"I'm near enough through." Molly stuffed a dust rag in her apron pocket. "You act like they're celebrities."

"They're real nice, Ma." His words rushed out in his excitement. "You'll be friendly to them, won't you?"

Molly's mouth turned down. "When was I ever rude to anybody?"

"Sorry, Ma." He gave her a quick hug. "It's just that these people are special." He stopped talking as the soft sound of footsteps crossed the front porch.

Molly looked past her son and saw a man, woman and teenage girl, who except for their age and gender, looked almost exactly alike. She saw at once why Joey had been so captivated by them. They were tall and slender, with wavy hair that was the color of corn silk, and blue eyes that looked as big as half-dollars. They stood as straight as toy soldiers.

Molly smoothed down her apron. Suddenly she wanted to change her dress and brush her hair. At the same time, it irritated her that these show people made her feel shabby.

"Ma," Joey said grinning, "this is Mr. and Mrs. Miller and Bonnie." His dark eyes twinkled. "They have a diving act—climb way up on a ladder to a platform and dive into a little pool of water."

"If the rooms are ready, Ma'am, we'd like to rest a bit," Jake Miller interrupted.

"Bonnie's been tired all day," his wife added.

Joey picked up the suitcases and showed the Millers their rooms. He stopped outside the girl's door and they talked quietly.

Molly was peeling potatoes over the sink when Joey burst into the kitchen whistling. He came up behind his mother and untied her apron, letting it fall to the floor.

"Pshaw!" Molly exclaimed. "You put that back on me this minute, young man." Her brown eyes were stern.

"Just kidding, Ma." Joey smiled. "Wasn't I right about the Millers?"

"They seem nice enough." Molly was silent for a minute. "Joey, don't let yourself get too wrapped up in these entertainers." She wiped her wet hands on her apron. "They'll only be here for a few days."

"Please don't spoil this for me," Joey said. "The Miller's aren't like other show people."

"I just don't want you to get hurt, that's all."

"Mr. Miller said he'd show me around the circus tomorrow," Joey rushed on. "He's gonna introduce me to the performers and let me watch them rehearse."

"You be sure to do your chores before you go."

"Yes, ma'am." Joey left the room, letting the door slam behind him.

The circus was scheduled to stay in the fallow field between Eufaula and Clayton for four days. The biting cold and rain didn't alter its plans. As the days passed, Joey and Bonnie were almost always together. The little time Molly had alone with her son, she tried to pamper him. She cooked his favorite food, but he only picked at it. When she warmed his blankets by the fire at night, he took them down the hall to Bonnie.

Molly saw that her coddling irritated him. "Call me Joe," he reminded her time after time.

^ ^ ^ ^ ^ ^ ^ ^

After school on Monday Joey went straight to Benson's pasture to watch the afternoon practice. When it was over, he walked home with Bonnie and her parents.

"Do you think I could ever learn to do a diving act like yours?" Joey took long steps to keep up with Jake Miller's stride. "It looks like a lot of fun."

Jake was quiet for a minute. "It's not all fun," he said at last. "There's some danger involved."

"When I was little they had to make me jump," Bonnie said almost in a whisper. "I was so scared."

Joey didn't notice the sideways, squint-eyed glare Jake shot toward Bonnie. They had reached the house now, Jake leading the way. He climbed the front steps and crossed the porch in front of the others. "This cold weather is making me ache," he said over his shoulder. "I think I'll lie down a little while." He and his wife went upstairs to their room.

"I wish I had a family like yours," Joey said, looking intently at Bonnie as if he were trying to take in her beauty all at once. "I don't even remember my dad. He died in the war when I was five. You and your folks seem so close, working together and traveling all over the country."

Bonnie's smooth brow furrowed. "We're a fifth-generation circus family. I wish we had a house and could stay in one place," she said. "Your Ma makes a nice home for you."

"Joey?" Molly called from the kitchen. "Is that you?"

"Yes, Ma," he answered.

"Will you bring in some wood and start a fire? I'm late getting supper fixed."

"In a minute," Joey said.

Bonnie looked at Joey and smiled. It was a soft, sad smile. "You go ahead," she said. "I need to rest anyway."

Joey was silent as he built the fire in the potbellied stove. "I'm worried about Bonnie," he said to his mother at last. "I don't think she feels good." Then with a quick grin he said, "Could you mix up one of your concoctions to make her feel better?"

"I can't cure anybody until they get good and sick." Molly returned her son's smile. "What she needs is to stay out of this weather and get plenty of good food and rest. I'll make her some potato soup if you think it might help."

^ ^ ^ ^ ^ ^ ^ ^ ^ ^

The bad weather got worse. On the third day Bonnie started to cough. By that night she was flushed, and Molly was sure she had fever.

"You're not going to let that child dive in this weather, are you?" Molly asked Bonnie's mother.

"Oh, she'll be okay," Helen Miller chuckled. "Bonnie's a lot tougher than she looks."

"Why don't you let her stay and rest tonight?" Molly urged. "Maybe I can do something for her cough. I nurse a lot of my neighbors when we can't get hold of Doc Baker."

"The show wouldn't be as good without her," Helen Miller said and left the room.

Molly waited up for them that night. When she saw the girl and heard the gravelly breathing, Molly knew Bonnie had pneumonia. "It's too late to get the doctor tonight," she told the girl's parents. "Joey can go for him in the morning."

At daybreak Molly was in the kitchen stoking the fire. She glanced up and saw Jake Miller standing slump-shouldered in the doorway. He held out an envelope. "This is all the money we have," he said. "Use it to take care of Bonnie." Molly saw tears in his blue eyes. "The circus is leaving today. We have to go. If we don't, we'll lose our job—won't be able to get another one." He paused. "Bonnie understands." He turned quickly and walked out of the room.

^ ^ ^ ^ ^ ^ ^ ^

Doc Baker came early in his tan Ford, one of the few cars in Barbour County. He was a tall, wiry man with a serious look about him, and a slow, easy manner. He examined the girl, and then called Molly aside.

"I've done all I can do, Molly. You were right; it is pneumonia. Her temperature is up to a hundred and five. If there was a hospital close by, we might do something, but I doubt it. You know as well as I do pneumonia has to run its course." His voice trailed off. "I'll show myself out."

It was almost dark as Molly and Joey began their vigil over the dying girl. Mother and son sat silently by Bonnie's bed. The sparkle in the boy's eyes had been replaced by a vacant stare. Outside the freezing rain fell steadily, and the wind slammed the shutters against the house. Molly bathed the girl's thin wrists with alcohol, trying to bring down the fever, while Joey stoked the fire.

"Ma, is she going to die?" Joey whispered, breaking the silence.

"I'm afraid so," his mother answered.

"Can't you help her?" he pleaded.

"All we can do now is pray."

"How could her parents leave her?" His voice was louder than he meant for it to be.

"I guess I don't understand that myself, son," Molly said. "Try not to be too hard on them. Things happen sometimes that we can't control—like when your father went away. He didn't want to leave us, but he had to go. And when he left, he didn't know that he wouldn't ever see us again."

"That's different," Joey insisted.

"Not completely," Molly said.

"Pa didn't have a choice. He wanted to stay, but they made him go," he argued.

"We don't always have the freedom to choose to do what we want." Molly spoke softly trying not to disturb the sleeping girl. "Sometimes our choices are made for us by circumstances—by work as well as war."

They were quiet again.

^ ^ ^ ^ ^ ^ ^ ^ ^

Bonnie was dead before the new day was light. Molly had her buried in the pauper's section of the graveyard, using the small amount of money Jake Miller had left. A sane look returned to Joey's eyes, but he remained silent after the funeral. He went straight to his room, refusing to eat.

Molly made herself a light supper, eating only out of habit. She wanted to go to Joey, to tell him she was truly sorry about the girl. She wanted to comfort him, to say something to ease his grief. She cleared away her dirty dishes and walked softly toward his room.

As she reached Joey's door, Molly stood still. From inside the room she heard the dry, hard smothered sobs of her son. She reached out and turned the doorknob, pushing the door gently open. It was the crying of a man that she heard. Molly silently shut the door and crossed the hall to her own room.

"Goodnight, Joe," she said.

# Weeds

## by Budge Breyer

For the public view,
For visitors and passers-by,
For neighbors' sake and so as not to shame
The family, especially the wife,
The front should be kept tidy –
Lawn mowed, borders straight or curved not straggly,
Hedges trimmed.

But to my mind somewhere in the back
There should be one spot, one private high-walled patch
Untampered with, above all unweeded.

Weeded? Weeds? Weed?
Weed is not botany but bigotry
Born of arrogance.  What displeases us
Or inconveniences or even is
Where we have not intended it,
Planted it, commanded it.
The glorious, towering foxglove I have heard
Referred to as a weed
Because it dared to grow unbidden by the roadside,
But place it where we wish it,
Or squeeze it when we need it,
Give it a Latin name and it becomes
Beauty and juice invaluable,
A pleasure and a treasure.

Or take the dandelion –
The word itself a blessing of our mother tongue
Upon a name whose foreign source
Gives notice only of unlovely leafage,
Ignores the splendor truly leonine

Of sunburst bloom.
And when that golden sun decides to set
It grows its own immortality,
Turns full moon, a silken silvery sphere
An infant's breath can shatter into stars
Which fall to earth and rise as suns again.

And so into this patch I have in mind
(Somewhere in the back)
I welcome weeds, whatever seeds or spores
The winds of heaven blow or birds bring
In beaks and bowels. Here let them grow
Their splayed leaves and fungoid blobs
And ropes of vines and twine
And tangle till they strangle one another
Or mate somehow and mutate
Into a new creation!
For such, so it can climb and scare the world,
I'll so far break my rule and tamper with my patch
And build a trellis there. A better one than this.

# Eugene
## by Mary Helen Brown

Edward Eugene Bishop's story is hard to tell, partly because he changed it regularly. But, as he often told me, "you can always make a good story better." I'm lucky to know much of his story at all. Most folks were so intimidated by him that they avoided long conversations. His four older daughters would tell the youngest how lucky she was that her daddy was old when she was born and not as mean as their daddy. His five sons-in-law would try to top each other with tales of the many ways their lives were threatened if anything happened to his girls.

Most of his grandchildren lived in abject fear. They would run, not walk, when they were within reach. He would lunge, roar, and try to grab them. If successful, he would look down and snarl, "You know alligators eat their young." They would scream, cry, wiggle free, and run. I thought it was funny and let him hold me, roar, and toss me to the sky. He was my Granddaddy Bishop, and I adored him. My cousins and sister still think I'm crazy.

Granddaddy Bishop left me with stories about his life, his wedding ring, practical advice, his barber's license and four straight razors, a large framed photograph of his hero, Will Rogers, a trunk he made as an apology, and an essay. He was working on the essay about the time he had the stroke that killed him.

But to understand the essay, you have to understand his story, and his story is hard to tell.

His mother outlived her husbands, but, even so, died when Eugene was in the 3rd or 4th grade. He was orphaned with two younger brothers, Will and Jack. At first, they lived with family members, at least one of whom abused the boys, especially Eugene who took most of the beatings to protect his brothers. Eugene ran away, quit school, worked in the sawmill, and lived in barns when he could and outdoors when he couldn't until he had enough money to rescue them.

He supplemented his mill pay by bare-knuckle boxing and "rasslin" full-grown men in the swamps of Louisiana. He took a lot of beatings and occasionally won. That's how his brothers could stay in school and still have money for food and a place to live. His brothers ate first, and he would eat what was left or what he could scrounge.

Most accounts allow how Eugene was the strongest fellow in the parish. The story goes that one time a piece of machinery had broken off and jammed in the saw works. Three men working together tried to dislodge the piece. Finally, Eugene, still a teenager, growled, "Move the goddamn hell out of my way," and jerked the works free.

As the years went on, he began making better pay at the mill and won more of the unregulated matches. When he believed his brothers could care for themselves, Eugene struck out for Mexico to look for gold. He claimed to have found it, but had been robbed on his way back to Louisiana. Otherwise, we'd be rich.

The version of the story he told me went something like this: "I was on my way home and was just bone tired, so I went to sleep on the side of the road. I don't know what woke me up, but there was this six-foot tall jackrabbit coming at me, trying to kill me. I wound up having to beat that son of a bitch to death with a broom."

Needless to say, knowing Eugene's tendency to embellish a story, there is great doubt that that, or any other, version was true. Most of his stories seemed to be some amalgamation of *The Treasure of the Sierra Madre* and *Harvey*. It wasn't until his funeral that his brother Jack told us that the story was mostly true—that Eugene struck out walking to Mexico to prospect and while there hit a strike. On his way home, he was robbed, beaten, and left for dead by a gang of bandits. Jack said that they didn't hear from him or know what happened for a long time.

Eugene was a handsome, strapping young man with blond hair and blue eyes. After his prospecting venture, he'd gone back to the sawmill, this time as foreman. He likely would have been quite a catch except that most folks feared him and his temper. One who wasn't afraid was a local, circuit-riding Methodist preacher who saw something in Eugene worth saving. He took to inviting Eugene over to preaching and Sunday dinner. After several invitations, Eugene took him up on the offer. He thought he would tolerate the preaching in exchange for a chicken dinner.

The regular parishioners were shocked the morning when the roughest man they knew walked into the parlor that doubled as a church. Eugene greeted them with his usual courtesy, "What the hell you lookin' at?" and sat right up front to spite them all. Then his life changed. He saw the piano player, the reverend's daughter, and "the prettiest little thing" he'd ever seen. He found the preaching to be tolerable and the dinner to be delicious. Thus, he set forth with his usual stubbornness to make himself acceptable to marry Reverend Sheppard's daughter, Iva Mae. That he did so scandalized most of the community except for the

Sheppards who treated Eugene as another child, albeit a much rougher version than any of their others. Over time, two of Iva Mae's sisters married Eugene's two brothers, resulting in a gnarled family tree consisting of double first cousins once, twice, and thrice removed.

The Sheppards helped smooth Eugene's edges, but just a little. Mainly, Iva Mae, all of 4'10" and 95 pounds, ruled the household and saw to it that he didn't actively threaten the townspeople. Reverend Sheppard taught him the wonders of books, and Mrs. Sheppard taught him about flowers. He no longer sensed a need to fight everyone—at least not all the time.

The company sent him from mill to mill as the timber was exhausted. Eugene's first four girls were born in three different logging towns. These logging towns were barely civilized, and the reverend's daughter got good at letting people know that she knew how to use her shotgun. And, besides, if anything happened to her or her girls, they'd have to deal with Eugene.

Even so, the story goes that a young man took advantage of one of the girls. The fellow's daddy was the richest man in the parish, and he felt he could have anything he wanted. I was never told what exactly happened, but Iva Mae had Eugene put in jail before he could "kill that boy" because, "by God, he would have." She knew that between the boy's money and Eugene's reputation an execution would have been inevitable. So, Eugene was locked up until the boy could get out of town.

Eugene quit the lumber business, polished a skill he had acquired, moved to North Louisiana, and got his barber's license. He and Iva Mae also had a fifth child, another girl, my mother. He and my grandmother raised the five girls in a three-bedroom one-bathroom house near a trolley line. He eventually became the first-chair barber at the Captain Shreve Hotel. The Captain Shreve was located reasonably close to the Municipal Auditorium, the home of the Louisiana Hayride. Eugene took credit whenever anyone at the Hayride had a fine haircut, including folks like Johnny Cash, George Jones, Faron Young, Hank Williams, and Elvis Presley to name a few.

He never completely mellowed. His brother Will felt the full force of his fury. Will, the sheriff of a neighboring parish, was a complete bully. Once on a visit, he backhanded Eugene's "baby" for something she'd done. My momma told me that Daddy "went into a blind fury," "knocked him into the next room," "beat him senseless," "picked him up by the belt and coat collar," "threw him down the steps," and "kicked him all the way to the middle of the yard." If Will hadn't been his brother, "Daddy would have killed him right there."

Instead he settled for cussing him, telling him to "go to hell and never show his face there again." He didn't.

My memories of Granddaddy Bishop are different. They come from his small house and the barber shop he opened later in life. By the time I knew him, he was in his late 60s. He had had several heart attacks, but was still incredibly strong. We spent hours together, and he taught me more life lessons and skills than I have learned just about anywhere else. My more cowardly cousins will never know what all they missed. No wonder he'd look at them, then look at their parents and say, "I'd a throwed that one back if I were you."

We went on lots of adventures. He'd growl, "C'mon, we got to get away from these women," and we'd head off down the street with me reaching as high as I could to hold his hand. Sometimes it was just to meet the ice cream truck. He claimed that I could hear it when it left the dairy. We'd go walking around the neighborhood until we'd meet up with it. Other times, we'd come back hours later with me slung over his shoulder, sound asleep. He'd tell everyone that we'd gone to the park. Years later, my parents learned that we'd ridden trolleys and busses all over Shreveport and Bossier City and gone to ball games, museums, libraries, gardens, bars, and, on occasion, a park. This discovery was made when I seemed too familiar with a place. They'd ask how I knew about a place, and I'd say, "Granddaddy Bishop brought me."

Granddaddy Bishop enjoyed television, but he especially loved watching baseball. I'd sit with him in the big chair, and we'd watch the game of the week with Dizzy Dean. I picked up a lot of vocabulary from Ol' Diz—words like "slung," "brung," "threwed," "slud," and several others that completely unnerved my other grandmother, the schoolteacher.

Baseball games, boxing matches, and certain other programs were not to be disturbed, so we'd settle in to watch them while "the women" would gather up the fliers and head to Weingarten's and Brookshire Brothers to make groceries for the week. One day the phone rang and Granddaddy Bishop had to answer. He did so as usual, "What do you want?" A few grunts later he hung up, just hung up, never said good-bye, and we went back to watching the program.

When the women returned, my grandmother asked how we did. He replied, "Harriet [a granddaughter] had the baby." Many questions ensued.

"Was the baby a boy or girl?" "Don't know."

"How much did the baby weigh?" "Don't know."

Finally, "What's the baby's name?"

"You're not going to believe it."

"What?"

"You're not going to believe it."

"What is the baby's name?"

"I swear, it's Domino Nicoli."

"Eugene, you know that baby's name isn't Domino Nicoli."

"I swear it is."

Granddaddy even laughed. This discussion went on quite a while. Whether or not to call back to find out the answers to all the questions was also a source of debate. It would be a long distance call, and long distance calls were only for very special occasions, so Eugene was scolded for not getting the information on their dime. Oh, the baby? My cousin, Dominique Nicole. I still have no clue how much she weighed at birth.

As I said earlier, I learned a lot from Granddaddy Bishop. Here's some of the lessons he taught on our adventures and during "words from our sponsors." These lessons emerged from his life story, and I find them useful.

On throwing a punch: "Keep your thumbs outside your fist and aim a foot behind what you're hitting. There's no damn rules other than that the one standing at the end wins." I was small, and he didn't want anyone bullying me.

On being self-reliant: "Everybody's got to sit on their own bottom."

On eating: "Taste it. It can't be worse than hay. If you don't like it, don't eat it. If you do, it might keep you from starving sometime." I still like oysters.

On buying real estate: "Never buy a house in a hole." My current house is on just about the highest point in town.

On judging others: "Never think you're better than anybody. You're just lucky."

On self-righteousness: "Anybody who says he's never said 'shit' has never slammed his hand in a door."

On making others happy: "Jesus Christ couldn't please your grandmother."

On getting what you give: "You can stand up on a hill and yell 'I love you,' and what you'll hear coming back is 'I love you, I love you, I love you' or you can stand on a hill and yell 'I hate you' and all you'll hear is 'I hate you, I hate you, I hate you."

On gardening: (His flowers won statewide awards.) "Nothing grows camellias better than cow shit." This observation meant that my mother and I annually filled the back of my other granddaddy's pick-up with manure from his farm and drove it an hour to Shreveport. The observation also would stun the curious garden club ladies into total silence, a most unusual condition.

On maturity: "It takes a long time to climb fool's hill."

On recuperating: "Nobody ever got better sitting on his ass."

On advice: "Always pay attention when a feller's telling you what you ought to do. Then decide if you're smarter than him or he's smarter than you. If you're smarter than him, go about your business. If he's smarter than you, you might learn something."

When I was 13 my granddaddy had a massive stroke that the doctors said should have killed him immediately. He lived about six more weeks out of pure-d stubbornness. After he died, the family found a notebook containing an essay he'd written. The essay stops in the middle of a thought. It may be that he was writing when he had the stroke. My mamma wound up with it and gave it to me because she said it was meant for her and me. It's his philosophy of life and his final lessons. I've copied it here, preserving as much of his spelling and grammar as I can make out. I decided long ago that I may be more educated (and was even at 13), but he was smarter than I'll ever be.

*The World does not care any thing of us as indivigials unless we have as an indivigial performed some great feat such as paint a picture, erect a great Temple, Building, monument, Cathredl or Dam, created a nation or Empire which would be utterly impossiably for each and all of us too do, but we and all too the least of us can leave our best thoughts or ideas or those events that has made the most lasting impression on us during our live, this I shal attempt to do as I live from day to day from a very humble childhood shal I say proverty stricken existence I as chaild could never tolerate any, but the most conjeanial attmosphere. The power of consecration is in its self a great acheavement I mean by this is to be able to shut yourself out from the noises and confusion all about you & to think your own probums through. My own personal expexiance was to go to school too an old ex army Captain who maintained strictdiscilpian in others words there was no time for idleness you must keep your mind on your work at all time for this was the day of corpral punishment which is unknowed today in the school room but he did teach me self control for which I have been very thnkful otherwise I would have distroyed myself at an earlier date unless we as indivigals can avoid as much stress & strain as possiable we can not hope to live a very sucesfull life or a very long life for we find we are being constantly obstacted or diverted from our objective.*

*Many men are flustrated for the simple reason that they have no Fame or acclaim to challenge them too their Best effort this I have always tryed to avoid it has been my lifes ambistion to be of some service to my comunity or my fellowman and not a religeous bigot or a race preduiced Heathen. I have alwyas tryed to be, selfsufficient, cakepable, suffient, competent, reliable able, independent, and my life ambition has been in too instill theas same virtures in my family and foremost and always a loyalty too. Family and to country & sivalization with the knowledge that no member of the Human family has any privelage or moral sight to debase or degrade society or Humanity. And as I approach the last few years of my life I do not offer any excuse for being a failure neither do I seak any reward for my efforts I only hope that in some way I may have in some misterious way of some service to humanity.*

*I am opposed to any compromise of any moral princiable though one must coropeate with others in endevor there is many part to one's life he must be able to work, play, laugh, love, hate, fear, enjoy, seak, avoid, but gratest of attrabutes of many is courage and not pride or vanity or I may say that courage that is form of love courage with out love is a force with purpose. Courage to do the right or honorable thing regardless of purpose or person.*

# The Monarch
## by Joseph A. Buckhalt

U.S. Highway 231 runs from Panama City, Florida, to St. John, Indiana, a distance of over nine hundred miles from the Gulf of Mexico to near Lake Michigan. I did not know this fact in 1957, when I was eleven years old. But I was intimately familiar with one short section of U.S. 231, the 100 block of North Oates Street in Dothan, Alabama. For in the middle of that block, on the east side, was Monarch Dry Cleaners. It was situated adjacent to the Masonic Temple, a massive yellow brick structure that made Monarch seem very small in comparison, bookended at the other end of the block by the Houston County Courthouse, another marvelous yellow brick edifice that had been erected in 1905. The date of its construction was another of many facts I did not know in 1957, and neither did I know that the courthouse would be demolished just a few years later to be replaced by a charmless but modern rectangular box of a building.

At home, we called Monarch "The Plant," a name that strikes me now as rather anonymous and strangely impersonal given that my father and mother were the owners and operators. They spent a lot of time at Monarch, as it was open six days a week from six a.m. until six p.m. My father would arrive first, around dawn, to fire up the steam boiler that ran the presses. In the summer, Mother and I would go in later, and I would often take a sandwich made from an egg for which I had no early appetite. To wash down my egg sandwich, I would get a bottle of Coke from the ice-water filled red drink box in the back of the building.

One of my favorite tasks was operating the machine for encasing the cleaned and pressed clothes into plastic bags. Thin plastic from a large roll would be drawn down over the clothes, and then the exciting part came. Pulling down hard on a large handle brought heated coils in contact with the plastic, and sealed the bag at the top. A sizzle and sharp odor emanated from the burnt plastic, and after isosceles-triangle-shaped scraps were peeled off and discarded, a clean and neat bag covered the garments. My emotional memory is one of satisfaction in completing the day-long process that began when the dirty clothes had been brought in by their owners in loose piles. The clothes had come in wrinkled, soiled, with a faint smell of sweat, and we had transformed them. The process seemed to me comparable in many ways to baptisms that I witnessed many times (and participated in once) at the First Baptist Church a few blocks away down Main Street. As the preacher always said as he lowered someone into the water and pulled them back up, "We are buried with Christ in baptism, and raised to walk in newness of life." Trousers that had a few hours ago seemed unworthy and unredeemable were now washed of stains and ready for a new beginning. We used cleaning solvents rather than the blood of Jesus.

Dry cleaning clothes was a process that involved powerful chemicals, considerable heat, and genuinely hard labor. Summers in Dothan were very hot, and Monarch must have been one of the hottest places in town. The hottest job was operating the steam presses where large exhaust fans ran continuously, sucking the heavy air outside into the narrow alley that ran alongside the building. This cauldron was the domain of a muscular man with a kind face who was a master presser even though there was no such designation for pressers. He had worked there since before my father bought the business six years back, and he was our most experienced and loyal employee. He and my father would sometimes have disagreements and he quit on more than one occasion, but he came back each time, saying " I cain't work for nobody but Mr. Archie."

He and I had a good relationship and we spent a lot of time together as I would often follow him around, listening to his stories and idly watching him work. Sometimes I would bring him a cold drink and peanuts or the salt tablets he had to take because of the long hours in the sweltering heat. The skinny white boss's son fetching snacks for the grown black man did not strike me as odd in any respect then. When he answered my questions about what he did in the war, I felt a little sorry for him when he told me he was a cook and not a combat soldier. Little did I know that black men had a narrow range of options in the military.

Now I have a much more nuanced view of our relationship and see that my innocence and youth enabled him to view me as different from the white adults with whom he had to play a highly constrained, subordinate role. He felt my genuine admiration and respect and even though he called me "Mr. Joe," he was able to relax around me. I could detect a difference between his demeanor with me and the way his face would go blank and his tone flatten when he talked to white adults.

When I first saw the TV version of *Master Harold and the Boys* by the South African playwright Athol Fugard, the shock of recognition was immediate and intense. The white South African boy spent afternoons in his parents' soda shop with Sam and Willie, adult black men who worked there. In the play, the boy was on the brink of manhood at seventeen, and a minor conflict with Sam cast in sharp relief the fact that their relationship had to change drastically to conform to the apartheid culture. My friend no doubt knew that our relationship would soon have to change as well, but unlike in Fugard's play, our transition was not dramatic. As I grew up, the enlargement of my range of interests and activities would lead me to spend less time at Monarch. He just continued to press. After I left home for college, my parents would tell me he asked about me frequently.

But back then each day, I would eventually embark on an outing, a route around what was without question the most important block in Dothan. Exiting the front doors I passed between the pair of faux stone lions that were the only clue to the name of the business. The lions must have been white once but now were dingy grey from the dust of North Oates Street. Occasionally I would hose down the sidewalk and I would give them a spray, but the grime was too embedded for them to ever come clean. My direction was always the same. First I passed by the Masonic Temple, a building unlike any other in Dothan. It was one of the largest buildings downtown, yet I never saw anyone going into or coming out of it, adding to the mystery of the place. What went on inside? What were the meanings of all the symbols carved into the facades? When I turned the corner, I made my first stop at Kimsey Sporting Goods, a store that sold 45's and vinyl LP records in addition to sports equipment, a combination I thought was perfectly natural. The smell of new leather baseballs and gloves was intoxicating as I ambled slowly through the store, touching things gently as I knew I was allowed to do. I only rarely made a purchase, as that was not my usual mission, and after a few minutes, I exited out onto the sidewalk to enter the adjacent back door of J.C. Penney. The best part about shopping at Penney's was paying, oddly enough. Once selections had been brought to a counter, the clerk would take the money and place it into a cylinder that would be whooshed up a pneumatic tube to the second floor. Minutes later, the receipt and change would arrive after its journey through the translucent tubing.

Exiting Penney's front doors I continued next door to Woolworth's, my favorite of the three dime stores that graced downtown Dothan. Little glass bins with tiny price markers held a vast array of toys, trinkets, school supplies, and on one occasion a plastic ring I bought for a girl who sat behind me in third grade. A huge assortment of candy was available, weighed out by the ounce and placed in separate tiny white bags. Boiled and parched peanuts were sold by boys on the downtown streets, but while delicious, they were common snacks on a level far below the fancier ones sold at Woolworth's. Only later did I learn that peanuts were not sold on the streets in every town. But they were in Dothan, for we were proudly The Peanut Capital of the World, complete with a fall festival, a parade, and a Peanut Queen.

From Woolworth's, I walked south past the Wadlington Hotel, where I would glance into the dim lobby wondering who stayed there. The much grander Houston Hotel was a block away, but I knew no one who had ever stayed in either place. At the end of the block was Newberry's, where I would always stop, and then I would usually cross Main Street to Kress, completing the grand tour of our dime store trio. I had typically spent my money by the time I reached Kress unless I was looking for something special not found earlier, such as another pack of Topp's baseball cards that might luckily contain cards of stars like Duke Snider or Hank Aaron among those of lesser known players.

My homeward route took me past the Martin Theatre, where a big hit that summer had been Elvis's *Loving You*. Looking at posters for coming attractions would occupy a few minutes of my time before I moved into the final stretch back to Monarch. I turned into the alley beside the theatre that separated it from the grounds of the Houston County Courthouse where huge magnolia trees provided dark green and brown fragrant refuge from the sun. It was in the courtroom that my grandparents sometimes sang Sacred Harp on Sundays. With windows open, ceiling fans buzzing, and paper "funeral home" fans beating time, men in starched white shirts with sleeves rolled up and ladies in hats would take turns leading the singing, calling out the songs only by their number in the hymnal.

Farther down the alley was the back of the county jail where I would glance up at darkened barred windows, but I never saw any faces looking out. Although the jail, like the hotels, must have had occupants, they were unknown to me. By that stage of the journey, the only interesting remaining stop was one I always relished. Along the alley were the back sides of Woolworth's and Penney's, and both stores discarded their trash there. Unwanted items of considerable variety were jumbled in piles—metal display racks, cardboard boxes of all sizes and shapes, and sometimes the most unexpected items. True treasures were occasionally there waiting for my discovery. Sometimes I would think that items had surely been thrown out by mistake, for they seemed perfectly good to me and no different from the merchandise that was so neatly displayed and priced inside.

The last leg of the trip was a more narrow alley next to Monarch that ran out to Oates Street. I would run my finger along the brick wall, careful to dodge the pipes sprouting from the walls that intermittently spat steam and hot water. Through the open cantilevered windows, the hissing sound of steam presses were like a giant's sighs punctuated with low-frequency groaning thumps as the pads were pulled down onto the damp clothes. Parked in the alley was our family car, a '56 black and white Chevy 210 with two unique features: a very long whip antenna attached to the rear bumper and a special license plate. My father was a "ham," an amateur radio hobbyist, and the antenna was a feature no other car in town had. Inevitably, I would give it a shake as I passed by and then pause to watch and listen as it swished back and forth making a zinging sound. If I shook it just right near the bottom, it was long enough that I would watch a wave travel all the way up to the tip. On the license plate in place of numbers beginning with 38, the prefix number for the county, ours had the letters, W4GNG. It was a very plain car, but it attracted some attention for those two novelties.

Entering the back of the building, I would deliver to the office what remained in my little bags, usually hard chocolate and soft divinity candy that my parents or anyone around would share. The office wasn't a separate room, but just a section separated from the front counter and cash register by a half wall. From the office, one could see or hear when someone came in the front door, and also see when a car stopped at the curb. Parking was not permitted on that block of Oates Street, but stopping briefly was allowed, so we would rush out to gather an armload of dirty clothes. Occasionally a customer would leave his car and come inside even though doing so was technically a violation of law.

In early adolescence one has only vague notions of the changes to come. After a period of relative quiescence during overly long days waiting to grow up, the body begins to stir and bubble and before long its accelerator kicks into a higher gear. A number of critical events occurred late that summer that would parallel my passage into puberty. The authorities informed us that cars would no longer be allowed to stop in front of Monarch, no matter how briefly. I can't recall knowing if they cited federal, state, or local ordinance, but it meant the end of doing business there, and shortly thereafter Monarch Dry Cleaners was moved across town to a new building and location said to be superior in many ways. Customers could now park in the newly paved parking lot. New equipment was installed and the place smelled of fresh paint and linoleum tile. The old drink box was discarded and replaced by a larger upright one that used chilled air rather than water. But we could not take the downtown city block with us, and I knew my days of ambling slowly along my favorite route had come to an end.

In September of that year we watched intently and listened to Walter Cronkite describe the events in Little Rock, Arkansas. The Freedom Riders did not come to Dothan, and it was many years later that I even heard about, much less understood, what happened over the next few years in nearby places including Selma, Montgomery, and Albany, Georgia. I do recall that there was some expectation that something might happen in Dothan. I had no knowledge of Dexter Avenue Baptist Church in Montgomery, but I knew Dothan's First Baptist Church very well, as I was there not only on Sunday mornings and evenings, but also on Wednesdays at prayer meeting where I would do homework on the comfortably cushioned pews. Ushers had been given instructions to block any black folk who might show up at the massive front doors with the idea of attending services. None ever did show up that I know of, but First Baptist had a contingency plan in place that no doubt involved calling in the police. The irony associated with putting a tenth of my allowance money in a little offering envelope for the Baptist missions in China and Africa was not evident to me at the time. From time to time missionaries would speak at our services and tell of the lives they were saving in exotic faraway lands. But we sent no missionaries to black people in Dothan, and they were not welcome in our palatial house of worship.

Only recently have I considered another irony. At Monarch, we cleaned the clothes of everyone, and I guess no one had thought to segregate the soiled garments by race of the owners. When clothes came to us, we comingled them in the cleaning solvents and in the dryers, and even hung them afterward in racially integrated alphabetic sections. Even though we had the obligatory two restrooms at Monarch, one for each race, we were guilty of textile miscegenation.

Many years later I became friends with a man about my age, and we were surprised to learn that we had both grown up in Dothan and our childhood homes were not very far apart. The route from my house to Monarch passed within two blocks of where he had lived. But we did not know each other then, nor could we have. He had attended Carver High School and continued on to Alabama State University before becoming a teacher and then a principal. My path through Dothan High School and Auburn University led me to become a university professor. Our lives were similar in very many ways, and we both were "from Dothan." But we had grown up in two different Dothans.

Downtown Dothan, like most places and people, looks nothing like it did in 1957. All of the stores I knew are gone, and while many of the buildings remain, the establishments lack the vitality and luster of what was once there. The

Masonic Temple still occupies the northeast corner of the 100 block of North Oates Street, and at the southeast corner stands the Houston County Courthouse. The courthouse has an exterior façade constructed recently in a style I imagine would be called neo-historic, but it looks nothing like the original one I knew. Few people now know or care that in the middle of the block was once a modest dry cleaning plant with a grand name.

# Conversation with a Crow
## by James Buford

For most of my life I have been fascinated by crows. For example, research has shown that crows are the brightest of all birds and possibly as intelligent as dolphins and chimpanzees, who get their own TV programs. They are consummate survivalists who adapt to their environment. They don't congregate in trees surrounded by people carrying double-barreled shotguns and wait to be blasted like the late passenger pigeon. They engage in organized recreational activities and are reported to play a brand of rugby. Crows play elaborate practical jokes on other birds, animals, and even humans. They are said to go beyond mimicry in their use of words and phrases although evidence of this is mainly anecdotal (and somewhat rare).

The more I learned about these intelligent and complex birds and their quirky and prodigious behavior, the more I wanted to know. To me, a crow was a bird I would like to sit down and have a beer with (figuratively speaking, of course). My feelings are not widely shared, however. Most people I know have no interest in the biology and sociology of crows or desire to have an up-close and personal relationship with one. On the other hand, the information I have gained from crow encounters over the years may be of interest to scientists, political leaders, and even ordinary people who search for meaning in life experiences. You may come to believe that crows really figure in to the larger scheme of things, or you may decide that in my quest for avian connections I spent too much time in the sun. In both cases you're probably right.

My first experience with crows was when I was a farm kid in grammar school. I found a baby crow that had fallen out of his nest and took it home. I named him "Crawford" and raised him on chicken feed and table scraps. When Crawford started flying around the house and dive-bombing the cat my mom said I had to turn him loose so he could live in his natural environment. I took him outside and tossed him into the air, expecting him to go into a vertical climb, maybe circle once, and head for the woods on the back forty. Instead he flew up into the oak tree in our front yard and established a permanent base of operations. He took most of his meals at the chicken feeder but would still land on my shoulder for whatever I had on me. Nuts, candy wrappers, coins, rubber bands, my hall pass—it never seemed to matter as long as he came away with something. For amusement he continued to dive-bomb the cat, whom my mom had also banished from the house. Every day when I would get off the school bus he would fly down and wait for me to empty my pockets.

One day he didn't make his usual appearance and I started looking up in the tree to locate him. Finding no sign of him, I headed for the house and noticed the cat sitting next to a pile of black feathers. I was devastated. "You ate Crawford!" I yelled. She just stared at me with a "What else is new?" look on her face and then ignored me while she pawed through the feathers. I put Crawford's remains in a cigar box and took him back to the place where I found him. Before the burial I held a brief memorial service. The line, "Crow, born of egg," from *The Loved One* starring Rod Steiger would have been nice, but that movie had not been made at the time. I think maybe I recited the 23rd Psalm or possibly "The Lord's Prayer," but I can't really be sure. The cat went with me and attended the service. I'm not sure whether she felt bad about eating Crawford or just wanted the last couple of bites.

On a brighter note, my experience with Crawford did leave me with some basic skills in relating to crows. I could tell that he preferred for me to talk to him in English, as opposed to saying "Caw," like my sister did. Just before he met his demise I am pretty sure he was about ready to hold up his end of the conversation. Of course I'll never know, but from that time I have always spoken to crows that way. But no crow ever answered me back, unless you count the myna bird at the Birmingham Zoo. I asked him how he liked his living arrangements and he said, "Who's on first?" That was his reply to everything I brought up, except sometimes he would sing "Take Me Out to the Ball Game." That was about as close as I ever came to having a meaningful discourse with a crow (or even a crow-like bird) until one day recently when I was sitting in my backyard swing eating a sandwich. I noticed a crow sitting in a nearby tree. Just to be polite I asked, "How's it going, crow?" Much to my surprise, the crow flew down and landed on the arm of the swing.

"Very well, thank you."

I resisted the impulse to say something like "Hey, you can talk," and decided to act cool like exchanging pleasantries with a crow was something I did all the time. "Would you care for part of my sandwich?"

"Don't mind if I do," he replied, biting off a piece of bread. "I'm glad you learned when you were raising Crawford that crows expect to be offered something." I wondered how he knew about Crawford, who had to be several crow generations back, but I decided not to pursue the matter because I still felt guilty over what happened to him.

"Yes, Crawford was a good crow," I said, hoping we could move on to something else.

The crow obviously sensed my discomfort. "Look, we know your cat ate him, but nobody's blaming you," he said. He went on to explain that crows keep records of hatchings, matings, deaths, etc., and investigate accidents for evidence of environmental hazards or foul play. They also take pride in looking after themselves and have a survival manual that is periodically revised and updated. Young crows have to learn the rules before they are allowed to leave the nest.

"Crawford didn't follow Rule Number 12, which is to observe a three foot no-fly zone when annoying a cat," he said, by way of example. "We have rules that cover everything. That's why crows don't usually get shot, poisoned, run over by cars, or eaten by cats."

I learned that crows are very conservative and tend to vote Republican, especially in presidential elections. "You should be able to figure that out by looking at the map," he said. "All those states Bush carried were in what you call Middle America. Crows are Middle American birds." I was a little skeptical about that and suggested Bush would have carried those states without the crows. Then he started to get edgy. Apparently crows think they have everything figured out and get flustered when you disagree with them on anything.

"Maybe Kansas, but what about Tennessee? If Gore wins Tennessee, he's the president. We delivered Tennessee. That's the real story of the 2000 election, not that debacle in Florida. The reason Florida was so close was that Jeb said it was a lock and a lot of retired crows in South Florida voted for Buchanan. Besides, we watched that recount. Every time they shook a Gore chad loose in Palm Beach County we pecked out two for Bush in Dade County."

Then he stopped talking. Something was bothering him.

"Why don't you tell me about it?"

"Well, I hate to bring it up, but there is one thing that grates. We don't get any respect."

"Why do you say that? I've always respected crows."

"Yeah, but you also believe in the Great Pumpkin, and to be honest, most people think you're a little strange. I mean respect from mainstream people like school kids, soccer moms, sports fans, and guys with real jobs."

"I suppose you have a point."

"You got that right. I think the crow should be the national bird. What have eagles ever done for this country besides look symbolic and whine about being an endangered species? Instead of having a survival manual they want a government program. That's where the spotted owls got the idea. It's bird welfare if you ask me."

He went on for fifteen minutes like that with a litany of things like no state birds or sports teams, the use of disrespectful words and phrases such as "crow's feet" and "eat crow," and the lack of any crow tradition in American literature. While I waited for him to catch his breath, I decided to make a case that things weren't really that bad but I had to chose my words carefully because he was already pretty worked up.

"Can I say something?"

"I suppose."

"The national bird is supposed to look symbolic, and the eagle has it all over the crow. If you want to be a state bird, pick one and start a movement. What about Tennessee?

"Look, Gore was already in trouble in Tennessee. Do you think we would get anywhere trying to recall the mockingbird? They have a 98 percent approval rating, not to mention connections with people like Patti Paige and Harper Lee. Give me a break."

"Let's try expressions, then. How about 'as the crow flies?' Sounds pretty respectful to me."

"I knew you would bring that one up. It's the exception that proves the rule."

I could tell I wasn't getting anywhere, so I decided to try the logical approach. "O.K., tell me if you agree that a crow is any glossy black bird of the genus Corvus." He got a suspicious look, but he finally responded.

"Only for purposes of discussion."

"The Baltimore Ravens."

"Well, maybe, if you buy the 'crow by any other name,' line of reasoning. I suppose now you are going to cover crows in American literature."

"You asked for it. I think it goes, 'Once upon a midnight dreary...'" That was about as much as he could take and he interrupted before I could finish the line.

"Enough, already. I shouldn't have brought up the respect thing in the first place."

"Or maybe you were whining. Very unbecoming for a crow."

"Whatever."

He started acting nervous and distracted and I could tell I had ruffled his feathers so I decided not to press the issue any further. I didn't want him to fly away mad. "Actually, I agree that crows don't get the respect they deserve, but I'm on your side," I began. "I'm going to look into the state bird thing and try to find one without a big following, like maybe the brown thrasher in Georgia. I'll also try to come up with a catchy slogan like 'Go with the Crow.'" That seemed to calm him down, and I could tell that he thought I had come up with some useful ideas. His tone changed from argumentative and scolding to friendly and accepting— almost like one crow to another.

"Well, I'm glad we had this talk," he said. "For a human you make a lot of sense. You should write something about crows in your next book and include that slogan. You'll have a best-seller and probably even get recommended by Oprah. Then you'll be a famous writer and people won't think you're strange anymore."

"Do you really think so?" I asked. He finished off the last bite of my sandwich, and paused before he answered. Then he gave me a sideways look and I noticed a mischievous gleam in his eye.

"Nevermore."

Then he flew off and I haven't seen him since. Maybe he'll come back sometime and we'll talk again, but I can't be certain. What I can say about carrying on a conversation with a crow is that they always have the last word.

# Wingflicks

## by Marian Carcache

When my mama took me out of school and decided to teach me herself, she bought a botany book at a yard sale and we proceeded to plant things randomly in the backyard. It wasn't until she was satisfied with my knowledge of types of plants and categories of leaves—with the discovery that the cashew is from the poison ivy family and that morning glories, like potatoes, tomatoes, peppers, and eggplants, are nightshades—that she decided it was time to move on to the study of insects.

Her master plan was to work our way up to genetics, the discipline she believed held the key to all truths. "If you can figure out genetics," she said, "then maybe you can beat fate. It's like having a magical amulet that will free you from the spell of the wicked witch, let you out of Rapunzel's tower, turn you back from a frog to a prince." Her philosophy was that if genetically you come from Irish travelers who were potato farmers and maybe even sheep thieves, as her family was, you could embrace all the strength and spirit of adventure that those genes held, but still create a noble bloodline with your mind. "People used to buy the names of nobility for a price. Read Thomas Hardy," she said. Mama had been a writer when she was younger and freer, but she had just stopped one day, defeated. She had thrown in the towel on the thing she was meant to be. I could see that, and so could she. With that background, though, she had no trouble teaching me literature, but sometimes I think she got lost in it. It was that side of mama's personality, the side that got lost in thoughts, the side that concocted ideas about things that other people didn't want to think about, that put division between her and the school system in the first place. It put a division between her and a lot of things, like an easier life. That's a whole other story, though. The one I started to tell was the one about what happened while we were still studying the bugs.

She had not allowed me to do the bug collection in fourth grade when I was still in public school even though it was considered a huge project and counted a large percentage of that nine-weeks grade. She did not believe it was okay to teach children that it is just fine to kill an iridescent beetle or a beautiful butterfly in order to make "points" in a teacher's book. The end result was that the teacher made an exception in my case and let me do a photography essay on bugs instead of having to kill real ones and pin them to foam board. My project was so good that it was sent to the nearby university and passed around to seniors studying to be teachers as an example of a "new idea." Furthermore, my project did not stink as did the others after a few days in the hot classroom. And my mother, whom the rest of the world thought of as odd, was once again a heroine in my eyes. But inside every heroine, I've learned since, is a vulnerable and scared girl trying to follow a cryptic trail of bread crumbs left behind by some old crone who may or may not be wise, who may or may not wish her well. Mama wanted things to be different for me. I see that now. Now I understand that if she made mistakes bringing me up, it was because she wanted things to be different for me—the way all parents do. She wanted to leave a different kind of trail for me.

One day, a few weeks after we had started having school at home, I found her staring out the window with the botany book open on her lap. I couldn't tell whether or not she had been crying, but she was definitely deep in thought and a sad mood had settled on her heart. I lifted the book from her and read a passage she had highlighted:

*Male cicadas have a pair of tymbals on the first abdominal segment. Their abdomen is a hollow, resonating chamber. The female produces timed wingflick signals of broad-frequency sound, something like a rustle or a pop. The wingflick has both a visual and an acoustic effect. As a matter of fact, their song sounds something like the word "pharaoh." Sadly, some of the females die only partially emerged from their nymphal skins.*

When Mama met Eddie Pharaoh, I think she was afraid of dying only partially emerged. Of course, she didn't put her feelings into those exact words, but Mama was beginning to show her age. She was still pretty to me, but in the way a rose is still pretty after it's been beaten down by rain or tossed about by the wind. She said she no longer recognized the face she saw in the mirror, and wasn't sure about anything anymore. She said life was beginning to take its toll. I could tell she sensed that there was something in Eddie that could make her sure again. At the same time that she sensed that feeling about Eddie, though, it scared her to think that she could find the person who held the key to her wholeness and then maybe lose him. She had lost keys before.

My father, for example, was a mystery to me—someone she would not even talk about. It wasn't like it was with other kids who didn't have fathers around. My mother never seemed angry with him. She never talked badly about him. She just wouldn't talk about him at all.

Eddie Pharaoh had come with the spring. Mama said he appeared like a god in the middle of the road in front of our house. She was sitting on the porch alternating between pulling up briars from the flowerbed and making mosaic garden tiles from broken dishes, and had a clear view in all directions. She swears he didn't walk up from any direction; he just materialized and asked if she needed help with the yard work. Her hands were bleeding from either the briars or the broken glass, she said, and she noticed him staring at them. When she asked what he charged to mow, he said, "How about a cup of Joe?" It wasn't long before Mama had fixed up an old camper in our backyard for Eddie Pharaoh to live in. That first night that he lived there, he built a fire in a barrel in front of the camper and pulled chairs around it. Then he brought out a guitar and began to play. When he noticed Mama and me looking out the backdoor at him, he motioned for us to come join him. He'd already arranged enough chairs around the barrel for the three of us. I looked at my mama that night, illuminated by the flames from Eddie's fire, and saw the life coming back to her. I knew right then that no matter what else Eddie did or didn't do, he would see to it that my mama didn't die partially emerged.

Later, Mama would tell me that the months we spent with Eddie Pharaoh were much more valuable than anything the school curriculum could have taught me. "You were learning about life, Memorie, about things that *mattered* from Eddie Pharaoh—we were not just learning to take multiple choice tests." She went on for a while in her rambling way about what we learned from Eddie and I quit paying close attention to what she was saying, but this much I do remember. She said, "Descartes said that to understand a rainbow, he had but to study a single droplet of water. Eddie was like a torrential downpour of single droplets that we were allowed to learn from for as long as it lasted, even if we were uprooted by it toward the end."

That summer Eddie planted a corn patch behind our house, and he trained the wild muscadine vines onto arbors and tended to them so well that they bore a bumper crop of wild grapes that year. He told Mama that the corn was Silver Queen, and that she was a queen, too. He made her a crown of cornhusks and muscadine vine and crowned her: Miranda, Silver Queen of the Corn Patch. He taught her how to make wine in a churn and they also made dozens of jars of jelly. He said he worked in agriculture in another life. Had even joined the Peace Corps and traveled the world teaching people in poor countries to grow crops that would sustain them. The longer Eddie stayed around, the more lives we heard about. He told Mama that every time things hit rock bottom, he picked up the pieces and put his life back together again. He also told her that the day she invited him into our lives, she had saved his soul. He said when you've had to reinvent yourself as many times as he has, sometimes your soul gets lost in the shuffle, but that she had found his and given it back to him. Mama looked radiant that night, as if she really were a silver queen. What she enjoyed most in life was saving things and putting broken pieces back together, making wholeness from fragments. That was the side of her that was grounded. I figured it probably came from the potato farmer DNA. I sometimes wondered if our lives would have been easier if she'd just planted her feet firmly on the ground, if she had just been content to dig at the roots instead of reaching for the stars, too.

Later that night, back inside our house, we crawled into the iron bed Mama had salvaged from a junk shop and painted gold. We were lying there enveloped in the purple mosquito net she had devised around us, when, out of the blue, she said, "Memorie, have we ever talked about Plato?" Then she told me about how Plato suggested that at one time we were all attached to another being, but that we got separated when Zeus got mad and threw a thunderbolt and now we spend the rest of our lives looking for the other half that would make us whole again. She didn't say that night that Eddie Pharaoh made her feel complete, but I knew where that train of thought had come from. I wanted to ask her if anybody ever really found their other half, but I guess I was afraid of what the answer would be, so I lay there silent. The window was open from the top and I could hear Eddie's music playing in the backyard. Mama was silent, too, but I could tell from her breathing that she wasn't asleep yet either. Rod Stewart's gravelly voice came across the yard, through the scuppernong arbor and the rose bushes, through the chinaberry trees and the corn, singing about a mandolin wind. I knew that if I looked over at her, I would see tears streaming down her face in the moonlight, so I didn't look. I just lay there listening till we both fell asleep with Eddie nearby, keeping watch over us. I wondered whom the tears were for, my daddy or Eddie Pharaoh.

## II

At least once a week I asked Mama to tell me the story of her and my father, but every time I asked, she answered, "That's one story better left untold." It was unlike Mama to hold things back, and even more importantly, it was unlike her not to be fair to me. I believed that holding back the story of my own beginning was grossly unfair. I decided that the only reasonable explanation for not telling me about my own flesh and blood was that he must be a serial killer or kidnapper or subway sniper. Maybe he was a terrorist or a thief of anthrax.

In desperation, I finally asked her if he were some kind of monster that she didn't want me to know I was carrying DNA from, but she only answered, "Not at all," and then followed with a non-sequitur, "You have no choice but to follow beauty, but also wisdom because wisdom is the most beautiful thing. That is why I could not leave you in the school system. It would have frustrated your destiny."

When I had had as much as I could take of what I had come to view as Mama's nonsense, I went to find Eddie. Eddie knew how to say things that mattered in a way that didn't leave the listener searching for hidden meanings. I loved to listen to Eddie's stories about what all he had done before he came to live in the camper. He had lived so many lives that the stories never gave out. His were fantastic but, unlike Mama's ramblings, they had a substance, a foundation in the real world. He had been a fire jumper and had driven an earthmover; he had healed the sick and read the stars. "As a matter of fact," he said, "it was the stars that led me here."

"Do you think my father is in prison?" I asked, preparing myself to hear that I did, indeed, carry the DNA of the FBI's Most Wanted.

"I know he is," Eddie answered, "a prison of his own making."

Before I could dig for more information, Mama's voice cut the hot summer air like the howl of a banshee, causing Eddie and me both to jump. When it came to timing, she really did seem to have a second sight. Eddie sent me packing, dying inside to know more about my father. Mama was in the corn patch, holding that home school botany book from the yard sale, all charged up to do a lesson on club fungi. She was especially excited about rusts and smuts, having found some on the corn Eddie had planted. Maybe I imagined it, but when Mama read from the book that a parasite is an organism that lives on another living organism, she seemed to give special emphasis to the word parasite. Then without one line of transition, she added, "a parasite is a thing neither you nor I would ever want to be, Memorie. Parasites are a blight." After that cryptic comment, we began our lesson from the book and our "hands-on experience," as she called it, in the garden.

That night, as I stretched out on the glider and put my head in Mama's lap, I watched the fire end of Eddie's Camel and felt the glider move slowly back and forth as Mama rocked it. The night air smelled like gardenia and honeysuckle, and the crickets were busy somewhere in the night rubbing their hind legs together with all their might. I felt sorry that my poor daddy was off in a prison of his own making instead of being there that night with us. But I also felt happy to be a part of what I saw happening between my Mama and Eddie.

## III

After we went home and were in our own bed with the lights turned out, without prompting, my mama said, "Your father loved me, but broke my heart. And in doing so, he broke his own." We were both silent for a few minutes. I didn't dare speak for fear of breaking whatever spell had come over her and caused her to tell me something, anything. Finally, she continued, "The first time I saw him, we were both working a spring arts and crafts festival. I was selling mini ice sculptures and making enough money to get by. I had hit on the idea of freezing water that I had colored and flavored into shapes of things and selling them as novelty refreshment. It was a hot summer and people were buying my pretty frozen turquoise dolphins and pink lemonade mermaids to cool themselves down. He was blowing glass. He offered colored beads and glass animals for reasonable prices and his show really drew a crowd. Like everybody else, I was drawn to his performance. His gift for showmanship was remarkable. I couldn't take my eyes away as he heated the hollow tubes of glass until they were pliable and then gently blew into the open end as if he were blowing life into them at the same time he was shaping them into another, more interesting form, turning one more clear, hollow tube that was just like any other into something marvelous. There were winged horses and unicorns, crouching tigers and sleek panthers. To this day, I'm not sure whether it was the heat from his propane burner or some glitch in my own electrical hook-up, but I looked down to see myself standing in a liquid rainbow that was running from my booth to his. What was left of my inventory was running across the park. My booth was washing away and I didn't even care. When I looked at him, I felt like Dorothy, over the rainbow, face to face with a wizard."

"What happened next?" I finally managed to ask.

"Well, first he shaped me into another, more interesting form, for which I will always be thankful," she answered and then grew silent.

"And then what?" I mustered the courage to ask.

"And then what always happens with wizards once you see behind the curtain," she answered, but gave no details.

## IV

In the few months Eddie had been around, our whole world had transformed. Mama was still glowing and the thousand things wrong with the house had been repaired, one thing at a time. Even though we were in a late summer drought, the vegetable garden flourished and there were even roses now running on a trellis at the end of Eddie's camper. Eddie had taught Mama to shoot a target almost at dead center so that she never had to feel powerless, he said. Best of all, though, she didn't cry into her pillow every night anymore after she thought I was asleep. And I was pretty sure by this time that my DNA was acceptable, that I was not the bastard child of a Taliban terrorist. Even though the days were becoming almost unbearably hot, the music floated from Eddie's camper every night on the sweetest, coolest summer breeze, and all seemed right with the world. Rod Stewart was wailing out to Maggie May that the morning sun on her face showed her age, but that in his eyes, she was everything -- and my Mama's heart seemed lighter than I had probably ever known it to be. She was such a serious mama about some things, but there were the contradictions that never added up: having birthday cake in the freezer most anytime because we loved frozen birthday cake icing, eating beignets with chicory coffee with the heaviest cream for supper, but limiting our nightshades and refusing to drink with meals so as not to put out the Fires of Digestion.

It was without warning that the hailstorm came in the hottest part of August. I heard it before I saw it. Hailstones the size of pomegranates were hitting the roof of our house. When I ran to the window to look out -- this is the strange part -- I saw colored hailstones that were shaped like mythological creatures. Jagged bolts of lightning were splitting the sky, and every now and then a lightning bolt would split one of the hailstones before it hit earth. Those that made it to the earth sizzled and melted as soon as they hit the ground. And only seconds later, the colored streak of water left behind evaporated without a trace. But the strangest thing was that for several seconds each hailstone that fell left a streaked aura in the sky, so the world outside the window looked like a special effect from a movie. The storm came and went in a matter of minutes, and then the afternoon cooled off cooler than it had been in weeks, and the aftermath was beautiful.

Except that when it was over, Eddie was gone—just like my daddy, just like any summer afternoon heat storm. The camper was banged up pretty badly. We found craters in its roof that looked like a close-up shot of the surface of the moon. The glider had blown over, and the grill Eddie had used to cook on every night had been thrown into a tree and was mangled around the trunk. But the rose vine on the trellis at the end of the camper was untouched. It was covered with blood red roses the size of cabbages, and not a single bloom had shattered.

I begged Mama to call the police or to find Eddie on the Internet since she was so into research, but she said there was no need. She said men like Eddie don't want to be found, and that is what makes them rare and wonderful. "They're like the rainbow after a summer storm," she told me with tears in her eyes even as she tried to put on her bravest face. "Let's look up rainbows on the Internet and find all the ways they are like Eddie—they are the sunlight which has been spread out into a spectrum of colors and then diverted to the eye of the beholder by droplets of water." Then she started to assure me that Eddie would return in his own good time, but I could only think of my daddy, in a prison of his own making, who had not put in an appearance, for whatever reason, in my lifetime—and I blamed her for letting Eddie go, too. I blamed her for sitting there with tears in her eyes doing nothing.

"Shut up," I screamed. "You never make them promise you anything, and you drag me into it with you."

Mama was quiet for a few minutes. Then she said, "You are absolutely right, Memorie. I won't try to bend other people's wills, because we are not parasites you and I. We are not rusts and smuts who blight the lives of others. We want to be with people who want to be with us. So what would you advise me to do next?"

"Suppose I did know how to hold him here with us as tightly as a Venus flytrap holds an insect until it has squeezed its life out and devoured it. Is that what we really want?"

"Yes," I screamed, "that is what we want!"

Then just to hurt her I said, "Put me back in school so I can be like other people." Immediately I was sorry. I knew I had gone for her heart with that remark. If there was any way on earth for me to hurt her, it was to tell her that I wanted to be ordinary, that I wanted to be what she had set her heart against being. And I did realize that everything she said about Eddie leaving was true and that she could do little more than what she was doing without crossing a line she didn't want to cross. She was making an effort to embrace the calm after the storm. She was standing knee-high in the debris it left behind, hoping for a rainbow—the way she had done my entire life.

The next morning, in a weak effort to make up, I said to her, "We're lucky, Mama. We've seen what must be one of the most spectacular light shows observed on earth."

"I've seen it twice now," she answered as she handed me a cup of coffee with heavy cream so thick that it sat on top and didn't sink, and a piece of frozen cake, an end piece with extra icing. "And I have no doubt that it's not the last light show on earth, especially not for you. So learn from it. It beats the hell out of the SAT as a learning experience."

After that summer, my mama put me back in school. She stopped talking about her theories concerning DNA, standardized tests, the legal definition of insanity in Texas—and she couldn't listen to Rod Stewart again for a long, long time. But she took out her word processor and started back writing fiction. It was George Jones who kept her company late into the night for what must have seemed like an eternity to the timekeeper in her heart. To this day, I can still close my eyes and see her out on the screened-in porch, typing away at her stories, a cup of coffee and piece of birthday cake beside her, singing along with George Jones about it being "a good year for the roses."

But now there's Eddie, too, a little older, lying on the glider which they've pulled onto the porch, keeping her company while she writes, smoking his Camels and adoring the woman he came back to and found wholly emerged.

# Peaches
## by Wendy Cleveland

Today you brought me peaches
from the two farmers at the roadside tent,
their calloused hands resting
in wide denim laps,
sweaty bald Alabama Buddhas.

Inside the brown bag the fruit will ripen
yellow to orange and red
seam by seam, softer and sweeter
until the knife severs velvet skin,
the angle just so.

I will lift the wedge to your lips
kiss the juice and taste its sweetness
knowing there is more,
the pit lying on the wooden board,
halved fruit yawning wide.

# County Fair
## by Wendy Cleveland

based on the photograph "Ticket Booth: Central Alabama Fair" by Jerry Siegel

Earlier, fat men in straw hats strutted the midway
shooting ducks or tossing rings,
and a kid with thick glasses gawked at posters boasting
a two-headed lady and a man with no limbs.

Giggling girls groped through the mirror maze
as the barker lured curious men
behind the tent flap to watch Miss Penny
peel off leather gloves, grind and groove.

The frowning clown tripped over boaty feet,
his frizzy hair ringing a rubber pate
and all around children laughed,
reaching out to touch his ruffled cuffs.

Now, neon colors ignite the southern sky,
rides outlined in tiny globes of light.
Carousel ponies bob hypnotic up and down
under empty saddles of red and gold.

Ferris wheel buckets sway empty in the breeze,
and the operator leans on locked steel gates,
stale smoke smoldering between scarred fingers,
his teeth stained brown.

Haloed in their locked booth of glass
the aging ticket takers sigh and stare past
the darkened field of a small town
whose name they have already forgotten.

Tomorrow crews will fold tents,
pack up fat ladies and fortune tellers
in RVs swirling dust, and beer cups will fly
wind-blown from the whisted field.

# My Sister, A Girl
## by Peg Daniels

"Race you!" I say. Today I'm going to win, I can feel it.

Alice and I, dressed in our orange-and-blue swimsuits and "Eat My Bubbles" T-shirts, dash out of our house. We jump on our bikes and pedal toward the rec center pool, the early-June morning air sticking to my skin like flypaper. Al is already ahead by the time we're passing Ricky's basketball hoop. She gets to the big magnolia, and I'm three houses behind. I round the corner and try to put on speed, but I'm trailing by nearly a quarter block when she slams to a stop at the bike rack.

"So, hotshot, where were you, again?" she says.

Enjoy it while you can, I think. Boys get stronger than girls. I wouldn't dare say those words out loud. I'm going on nine and Al turned twelve and no one else is around, so those words would get me tackled and sat on.

Within minutes, tons of other kids have biked or been driven to the big red brick rec center, and they stand near us on the steps, talking and laughing. Al and I are still shy, though, and haven't made friends with any of them. We moved here to Auburn a couple weeks ago—for the schools, Daddy says—but before this we lived in Lanett, near the river. There, we sometimes played football and basketball with neighbor boys a year or two older than Al. But Al and I had the best times just us two together. We'd cook up our own fun—fishing with cane poles, skinny-dipping, catching snakes and salamanders and frogs. Al has been my best friend since the day I was born. At least, that's the way I think of it, and I think Al does too.

Coach drives up in his pickup. He lets us into the building, and we race inside and down the stairs. Al cuts right, to the girls' dressing room, and I cut left, to the boys'. One time last year at the Lanett pool, I looked up from where I lay on my beach towel to catch Al coming out the boys'. "I was just testing," she told me, running a hand through her super-short hair. When I asked, "Testing what?," she laughed—the kind of laugh that means you don't really think it's funny—and said she sometimes thinks she's a boy in girl's skin. She made me promise not to tell anyone, on pain of death. I told her it was okay, that I pretty much think of her as a boy. She smiled, and later that day she taught me how to throw a slider.

The dressing rooms lead straight out to the pool, and I go to my station, for lessons with the other Stingrays. Al is two stations over, with the advanced group—the Tigerfish. Al tells me I'll be a really good swimmer because, for my size, I have a big rib cage and big hands and feet, like paddles. Al says she has small hands and feet and narrow shoulders. She worries about this because she wants to be an Olympic swimmer. She also wants to be a scientist and is serious about school. One night late last summer, I told her I'd like to be an astronaut—we were on the family vacation at the new Space Center in Huntsville—but maybe I couldn't be because I didn't want to study as hard as she does. She said I'm a boy, I don't have to study as hard. She said this like she was mad at me. But then she smiled and punched my arm and said she'd be an astronaut too. She turned her face to the moon and said she'd take one giant leap for her kind. I'm not exactly sure what she meant.

At the end of our lessons, the instructors give everybody fifteen minutes "free time," and we jump off the low and high boards and horse around. Al and I have made a game of treading water in the deep end and ducking under when a diver hits the water; we watch the bubbles and the diver pop to the surface. She and I are like two smart fish at the side of a tank, and the other fish don't know we're spying on them.

A boy does a one-and-a-half off the low, but he didn't have his ties tight and his suit slips and we see his crack. Al and I laugh underwater. Al swims toward the deep end ladder, me following, and a girl hanging onto the ladder is laughing too. The girl puts her head to Al's and asks Al if she saw the boy. The girl says to Al that she's Jenny and she's thirteen. She asks if Al wants to come to her house.

I splash them. Al splashes back. Al says to Jenny, "That's my brother." She says it like she only puts up with me, but she throws me a smile over her shoulder. Jenny asks how old I am, and I say nine—even though it's going to be another three months. Jenny says she has a brother Jack who's ten. She says I can come to her house.

Al and I bike home and change into shorts. Al hollers at Mama that we're going to friends' for breakfast. Mama says uh-huh, but I don't think she really heard because she's watching TV while she cleans the house. That's her job, cleaning house and cooking meals and taking Al and me places. Al says that nowhere on her own birth certificate did she sign a contract to do housework and raise kids and she isn't going to. She says that at least the women on the soaps Mama watches are nurses, even if all they want is to marry a doctor—or maybe a patient who's been in a coma for months. Al says that if she has to get married, she'll marry a guy who's going to be in a coma forever.

Jenny's mama feeds us breakfast with eggs and plenty of grits. We watch TV awhile—*That Girl, Bewitched*—and then Jenny asks if we want to go roller skating. We've never skated, but we say sure. Jenny's mama drives out along Opelika Road to the rink, way past the place Daddy fixes cars. She gives us money to rent skates, and then she sits in a chair and reads a *Southern Living*. Al and Jenny go into the girls', for a long time. When they come out, Jenny is wearing red lipstick and blue eyeshadow. And Al has faint traces of red on her lips! Al shrugs at me and makes a face. Jenny's mama looks up but then goes back to her magazine.

On the rink, Al and Jack and I do a lot of hanging onto each other and falling and laughing, having a blast, but Jenny skates slow along the edge in her shift dress and flutters her lashes at the older boys. One comes and skates with her. Al and Jack and I roll our eyes at each other, and Al scrubs her lips hard with her fingers.

An hour or so later, we leave, and all Jenny can talk about during the drive is the boy. Al smiles—but it's one of those smiles you do for company; she's crossing Jenny off her list as a possible friend.

Jenny's mama takes us to what looks like a little wood house on Glenn Avenue across from the Baptist church. Jenny calls the place "the Sani-Flush," and Al and I laugh. We stand outside, and a man hands us our food through a window. I eat a footlong chili-cheese dog and a chocolate dip cone, but Al only eats half her dog—says she's got a stomachache. Too many biscuits at breakfast, if you ask me. After we use a jillion napkins to wipe the grease and chili off our chins and hands, Jenny's mama drives toward our home. But as we pass behind the rec center, Al has her let us out, telling her we'll walk the rest of the way. Kids have got up a game of football on the softball field, and Al says we should see if we can play, that maybe we'll find friends. The new boys shift from foot to foot and look at each other when Al asks if we can join, but then the biggest boy, a fourteen-year-old named Tom, says okay. Al and I get to be on the same side—only, since our side lost the toss, we have to be Bama.

The game is going great, Al proving she's no slouch—though when she laterals it to me a couple of times, our team gets mad because I'm the smallest and slowest. A while later, Al gets tackled. Like usual when a kid gets tackled, we all pile on. But when Al gets to her feet, her face is tight and frowny, and I get a bad feeling in my chest. Tom talks low to some of the other boys, and they look at Al and laugh mean. Al runs toward home.

Tom put his hand up Al's shirt! I know it! I punch him in the stomach with everything I've got. Then I tear after Al. At home, I tell Al I won't ever play with those boys again. I tell her we'll find other friends or just be friends ourselves. I ask if she wants to go to the pool.

She's still looking hangdog, but she's got chlorine for blood, so she can't say no. Going into the rec center ahead of us are our next-door neighbors, Miz James and little Stevie. Little Stevie tugs at his mama's beach robe and points at Al and asks, "Can I play with him?"

Miz James flashes us a smile, and I know she's thinking it's cute her four-year-old doesn't know his he's and she's. But Stevie's mix-up is Al's doing. The last two Fridays, Al babysat Stevie, and I tagged along. Stevie's a funny little kid, and we all had a good time—though I'll never let on to anyone that I liked playing with a baby. Stevie's gotten real attached to us, especially to Al. When Stevie first called Al a "he," she didn't correct him. Al's eyes had flown to mine, and I didn't correct him either. We all go downstairs, and Al signs us in with the lifeguard at the table. Miz James stays talking to another lady, and Al goes right, and I go left. "Al," Stevie hollers, "you're supposed to go that way." He's pointing toward the boys'.

Al stops dead. Her eyes flick to mine, but I don't know how to keep her secret safe. She smiles at Stevie and says, "No, I go this way."

She hurries away, and Stevie looks at me with his mouth hung open, but I hurry away too. Stevie says nothing more about it, but Al wears her T-shirt the rest of the afternoon, even while in the pool. I know that's so Stevie won't see her suit has a top.

In the late afternoon, Al and I are sunning ourselves on the pool deck next to the Jameses. I'm dozing, my ears tuning in and out to a Marco Polo game, when Al stands up and says she's going home, her stomach hurts worse than ever. I open my eyes, and they fall to a splotch of red on her towel. For a second, I think it's lipstick.

"Al," I say, "you cut yourself." Al starts checking, and I see blood smeared between her thighs. I shoot my eyes away.

I know what the blood means. Last spring, with her lip curled up as if this was the final straw, Al told me that know-it-all Cousin Brenda told her that because girls have babies, when they get old enough their bodies "go through a monthly cycle like the moon going through its phases," and at the end they have to bleed.

Al snatches up her towel and wraps it around her waist and trots away. The lifeguard calls, "No running," but Al speeds up.

I fast-walk to outside the girls'. "Al?"

Stevie comes to stand beside me. "Is he hurt bad?"

"Al's a girl, sugar," Miz James says from behind us.

I want to punch her in the stomach, make her take her words back! I want the whole day taken back. I want Al and me taken back to when I was Stevie's age and us two were fishing the Chattahoochee.

I hustle through the boys'. Al is on her bike, streaking down the street. I pedal after her, but I can't catch up. I burst into the house. Mama is standing outside the bathroom door telling Al not to be silly, that nothing's really changed.

Al flings open the door, red-eyed, angry-faced. "Everything's changed. My life isn't mine any longer." Al pushes past Mama into her bedroom and slams her door.

I want to follow her. I want to say, "Just stay you." I want to say, "It's only a little blood." I want to say, "Don't leave me."

Mama heads toward the kitchen and tells me to go get out of my wet suit, that everything's okay. I turn toward my bedroom, turn back. I knock on Al's door.

"Al, come play with me. Race you!"

I hold my breath. Hold it, hold it.

I have to take a gulp. I want to cry, but then I remember I'm too old. I run outside. A football is lying in our yard, and I pick it up, toss it in my hand. I hurl it at the slice of moon hanging in the sky.

# Hold That Smile
## by Mary Dansak

When I was twelve, I had a pet crow. That set me apart not only from every other twelve-year-old I knew, but also from the limits of my own imagination. I never dreamed of a pet so strange and fabulous, and even when he was in my life, sometimes he was hard to believe. Roscoe disappeared suddenly, and I still haven't gotten over it; I cry to this day to tell the tale of Roscoe. Nevertheless, I will bravely carry on.

I was one in a family of four. We had a house and two cars, and for that we appeared typical, but we were not. For one thing, there were the animals. We had dogs, rabbits, and hamsters, but we also had rats, ferrets, possums, tarantulas, squirrels, beavers, salamanders, snakes, turtles, and the hero of this little tale, Roscoe the Crow. Creatures aside, there were other signs that we were unusual. My father was a snake doctor, at least that's what I thought. He worked in Funchess Hall, an echoing building full of dead animals stuffed with sawdust, a docile Gila Monster, a six foot rattlesnake named Charlotte, and a creepy freight elevator with doors that clanged shut with such ferocity that the elevator itself is worthy of its own story. As for home, it indeed delighted with the aroma of fresh baked Chess Pie on some days, but on other days, the smell of formaldehyde and dried out jellyfish drifted down the hall. I was a very happy little girl in my eclectic house full of animals. You might even say I found it enchanting.

One day when I was twelve, my dad came home with a cardboard box, and as usual when I saw a cardboard box, my heart leapt. Inside any cardboard box toted by my dad, I would invariably find a sheet of newspaper, a smidgeon of dried up dog food, and a small heap of shredded twigs or rags, made to resemble a nest. Oh, what possibilities a makeshift nest offered! What a chance for my heart to burst with love for a new baby animal! I hoped for a baby squirrel; I had long since fallen in love with their little nut brown faces. I peeked into the box anxiously.

It was no baby squirrel. Instead I was confronted by the ugliest little creature imaginable: a nestling crow. A cruel cross between an old man and a rubbery fetus, with big black eye spots covered by a thin membrane, a scrawny neck attached to a flopping skull from which a small beak protruded grotesquely; it sure was ugly. With wings nothing more than crooked bones, the whole gnarly little package was wrapped in hideously thin skin, through which I could see its desperate veins pulsing. I took one look at the demonic little beast and fell in love, for I knew what became of ugly ducklings. He held all the beauty in the world in his beastly form.

While I may have been happy, my father was ecstatic. "It's a crow," he told me with a twinkle in his eye. "I had one when I was a little boy." That eye twinkle suggested that maybe he had had a magical childhood too, one that could be revisited with the introduction of a crow.

Although I did not see it then, there was a daunting wrinkle being creased into my own perfect childhood right then. My mother has a deep phobia of birds and all things feathered and fluttering. Here was my father gushing with unbounded excitement for an animal that my mother would not be able to enjoy, putting it mildly. Usually a pathologically sensitive child, for reasons I can't explain I simply did not consider how my mother might feel about the crow, which I went about raising with my father and brother like it was the greatest thing ever, which it was. I have also conveniently repackaged all memories I might have had regarding my mother's reaction to tarantulas and snakes being loose in the house. I have since heard her refer to those days as "another life." Not me, it was my life, and however selfish it sounds now, it was better with a baby crow.

I eagerly took my turn stabbing bread squares onto toothpicks, dipping them into raw eggs, and feeding the little crow. Unlike the dolls into whose strange triangle mouths I stuffed bottles, only to have to change their "diapers" when water ran through their hollow plastic bodies, the baby crow's little body transformed and he entered an awkward childhood. He grew stubby little fans of feathers, and although he still looked like a miscellaneous pile of sticks and rubber strings, he was an improvement over his earlier self. To my surprise, he quickly developed a feisty personality. When he heard our footsteps in the room, he opened his mouth and demanded to be fed. We obeyed, and fed him constantly.

Then came the day my father came home from work with the announcement that the crow had opened his eyes for the first time and looked right at him. Similar to a baptism, when you are marked as God's own forever, a bird's heart and soul belong to whatever it sees the first time it opens its eyes. From now on, Roscoe would think he was one of us, and nothing could change that. I believed in the power of imprinting, and I knew this was one bird that would never, ever fly away. There were absolutes. The world was round. Men walked on the moon. Roscoe would never leave.

Roscoe grew to be a teenager in a matter of a couple of months, and finally, he looked like a crow. Almost. He still had a little bit of what I teasingly called scrambled eggs in the corners of his beak. His eyes were blue, not yet the steely black they would become. Like a human teenager, he became rowdy. He played like a puppy, hopping across the den floor chasing Robert and me, fighting with us over treasures such as strings or rags. Sometimes I couldn't help myself, and I would seize his body in my hands, and laugh at his mock fury as he scolded me with his raspy caw and turned his head this way and that to try to bite me. As soon as I released him, he'd hop up on my leg or arm and content himself to sit with me calmly, holding no grudge. I loved playing with Roscoe, and most of the time, I forgot he was a bird.

Roscoe took to living in a make-shift roost, a branch protruding from a bookshelf to the windowsill. When he grew his real feathers and began flying around the den, it was time to move him outside. His release wouldn't be like the others, those bittersweet partings when we released other orphaned birds we had raised, cheering them as they flew away, but leaving me brokenhearted and crying. Roscoe would not fly away. My father told me so. This is the same father who, once when we were crawling around in a creek and a thunderstorm came up, told me to lay low like an alligator and we'd be okay. I did as he said and never once did I worry about getting struck by lightning. And never once did I worry that Roscoe would leave us.

We stepped outside, and my father flung Roscoe into the air. Eagerly, we watched as he flew up into a pine tree, where he was greeted curiously by the other crows. He passed their inspection, and after a few minutes Roscoe took flight, flew in a nice wide circle and returned, landing on my dad's shoulder, ready to go back in the house for his raw liver supper. But there was no more going inside for Roscoe. He was a real crow now. His eyes were black, his beak was sleek and sharp. He could fly, and he could sleep in his own roost outside. Best of all, he loved us, and we loved him. Sure enough, in the morning, and every morning thereafter, he greeted us by cawing at the kitchen window, demanding breakfast.

Seeing him in the wild world outside, I began to realize what a special friend he was. I had a big black crow, as loyal to me as our dog!

Whenever I went outside, he flew down from the trees, excited and eager to play. Already delighted to spend time outside with our dog Bowzer, Roscoe added an immeasurable element of happiness. Whether I was building a fort, playing in the clubhouse, or just sitting in the grass pretending, Roscoe and Bowzer were there by my side. While Bowzer was eager to be near me, he was not demanding. The same cannot be said for Roscoe. Roscoe wanted attention and he wanted to play. If I was having a snack, he'd steal my napkin. If I tried to read, he'd hop onto my book and stare into my eyes. He incessantly pecked and clawed at anything that occupied my hands, engaging me in tousles during which he'd growl and snarl like a puppy. How I loved the funny crow, and his proud and playful ways. I felt terrible the day I accidentally discovered his cache of shiny treasures he'd so carefully hidden under a log. Amidst his noisy and furious protests, I rolled the log back over the trove and swore I'd never peek again. He didn't always play rough. He could be affectionate, and would often sit on my shoulder, rubbing his head into my neck, purring. Yes, purring. I learned that crows growl, purr, and snarl as well as caw their kingly proclamations through the forests.

In his calmer moments, I ran my hands over his body, greatly intrigued by the strange feel of him. I touched his head, marveling at how small his skull was under his thick plumage. And his neck, skinny as a wire, I didn't see how it could support his head. His shoulders were strong and his wings were solid. He had a dusty smell, which comes back to me now as I remember the black-blue iridescence of his feathers, his awkward under-wing area, and oh, his eyes. Those eyes! Glinting, mischievous, how could solid black eyes display such powerful personality? Everything about Roscoe seemed laced with magic and wonder.

Yet Roscoe was real, and he was as much a part of our family as the dog. Like Bowzer, he chased the car when we drove away, we took both of them with us on weekend trips to play or camp at Mussel Creek, and when the time came for our annual trip to Orange Beach, he surpassed the dog's privilege and came with us. We stayed in quaint cottages by the bay, sleeping on sagging mattresses with rusty and squeaking springs, while Roscoe roosted in the pine trees outside, awakening us daily, as usual, demanding breakfast.

Around the neighborhood, wherever Robert and I went, we were followed by the dog and the crow. When we rode our bicycles to Zippy Mart for candy, they followed. Roscoe would wait on my bike's handlebars while we purchased our candy inside. People began to comment. "Did you know you have a crow on your rooftop?" asked a friend's mother, whose face grew frightened when that crow flew down from the roof to my shoulder. Sometimes, if Robert and I weren't around, Roscoe went out for his own adventures. As Roscoe's territory grew, so did the chance that he could frighten someone who did not expect a crow to fly down from the trees. My father arranged for someone from the *Opelika-Auburn News* to write a story about him, in hopes that it would avert any fearful reaction to Roscoe.

Roscoe was most uncooperative during the interview and photo shoot. He raised a ruckus with the dog, stole a piece of notebook paper, and squawked like a spoiled baby when we tried to convince him to settle down. The photographer almost gave up on getting a decent picture. Finally, Roscoe conceded to sit on the back of my chair, and the picture was snapped just as he whispered a crow secret into my ear.

When the story ran, I was embarrassed. I thought the picture made me look ugly, with my flat chest and oily hair. I found that picture recently and saw it for what it is: I am twelve years old. Roscoe is leaning over to tell me something and I am looking up at him and smiling, a smile of pure, unselfconscious joy, frozen forever in a moment where childhood and adulthood are about to collide. I am still in the world of magic, talking to my pet crow, my loyal dog is nearby. My parents are watching and laughing, there is a lovely woman from the *O-A News* writing a story about my very funny life, and nothing is wrong. Beautiful. Beautiful. Hold that smile.

A week later Roscoe disappeared. He did not wake us up demanding to be fed. We went outside and called his name, and he did not come down from the trees. We spent the next few days searching for him, to no avail. Oh how I cried, wrought with a terrible, fathomless sorrow. I could not stand for him to be gone. I wanted to play with Roscoe, to fight with him over a sparkly ring, to feel his hard little head against my ear. He had to come back. He had to. That was one bird that would never, ever fly away. He would never break my heart.

We never saw Roscoe again.

I cried and cried when I lost that crow, and I still cry to think of him now. Of all the pets I have lost, why do I still cry for Roscoe? Is it something bigger than the crow I mourn? Am I crying because he disappeared at the same time as my childhood—Santa Claus's retirement, my parents' ensuing divorce, all that magic and gold and safety and trust dead and buried? Am I crying because I'm hormonal and tired, or because my own children's childhoods went by so fast, and disappeared like my crow? There are so many reasons I could be crying over that bird, but maybe it's just because I miss my pet crow.

# Robin Lake

## by Melissa Dickson

My son, young enough to believe
he can catch a fish with his bare hands,
did catch one—a common carp raised
exultantly like a hand bell blinking
iridescent verdigris in June's brutal
sun. He'd let the fish go, only to catch
it again with equal bliss until I knew
the carp wasn't all a carp should be.
Between assaults it hovered, senseless

and oblique at the water's twisting
surface. Before I could rise, a trio
of near-grown girls surrounded
my son and his fish; one cried, *He's lost
a fin.* Chest deep in our busy lake, the girls
took turns fastening the carp under,
held plumb as a church pew's end,
while the fish, still a fish, whipped
against their hands. I sat at my post

watching, trying to think of a way to save
him, to save them both. Sat there till
the young women floated into giggling
girls again, and my child returned to the sand
fortress half-built at the foot of my chair,
and the fish drifted alone toward shore.

# Parked Under a Crepe Myrtle at the Public Library

by Melissa Dickson

I recall my ex-husband's ex-girlfriend naming
them Crepe Murder for the way we prune them tight, back to
the trunk, after the fall, so that they fill out, blooming like
parasols by summer. All spring,
the crepe myrtle wear their truncated wounds, startling as raw
amputations and every year
we do it again,  passing the seasons this way:
 wound,

     bloom,

        wound,

           bloom,

              wound,

                 bloom.


It occurs to me, as perhaps it has to you,
that it is always this way; the wounding
and the blooming coming and going
in their course, so that we come to know it
as surely as we know our own waking
and sleeping, so that we fall into the light
and the dark without asking, anymore, why.

# Amabala

## by Jeremy Downes

Your hair grew thick in the humid wind the day
we poured the truck across the floodplains
of Dixie-hearted states. Your German fingers
counterfeited autobahns—through the wheel,
through the chipmarred cup at the truckstop.

The vertical word, the word obscured,
or placed backward in mirrors, I don't remember
which it was, but—*Amabala*—you said, as if
the most natural syllables, things in the world,
as if saying in our quiet, correspondent speech,
Wie schön ist Panama!, a phrase that I'd
been mispronouncing three days straight.

And so we came home to the place we lived in,
a backwards Southern state of grace, of wistful minds
and our hearts' brief theft of time. *Amabala*
we could live with, familiar, like the sudden comfort
of deadly metaphorical clichés unmade and made anew—
the ironical affirmation of our nights in transplantation.

You're out of the country now;
I mumble your Chaldean magic to myself,
scribble epistolary charms against your absence:
Come home to *Amabala*; come home to *Amabala*.

# My Summer with Patsy, Dale, and Roy

by Virginia Mitchell Edwards

I was either ten or eleven when one summer day a man in a truck with a horse trailer hooked on back drove up in the dirt driveway beside our house. Daddy followed the man in and said he had bought me a horse. One of my favorite books was *Black Beauty*, which I had read many times, and I had wished for a horse though I had never ridden one. The one that was unloaded out of the trailer was bigger than pony-size but not as big as the mules we had around the farm. She was either a Paint or Pinto. My granddaughter tells me that one is black on white and the other brown on white. I really think Patsy, the name I gave her, had both brown and black spots or maybe they were just different shades of brown.

All the family gathered around the new pony. A used saddle appeared from somewhere, and my two grown-up, tall brothers started riding my Patsy around the yard. I told my mother, "Make them get off! They are too big to ride my pony." Indeed, their long legs dangled past the stirrups, and almost touched the ground. I wondered, "Just whose horse is this anyway?"

Finally I had my turn at riding. I don't really remember any specific riding lessons or instructions other than not to fall off. Perhaps I had seen enough cowboy movies that I could mimic my heroine Dale Evans on her horse, Buttermilk, quite easily. Before long I was riding Patsy up and down the lane to the mailbox, over to Mrs. Bell Robinson's to buy eggs when Mother's hens stopped laying, and to the Lippencotts', a ways down the road where I would have let Betty Jean and Bubba ride had they wanted to. It was on the road in front of their house that I was almost thrown off Patsy. A horse fly bit her on the hiney and she suddenly bucked a couple of times and almost threw me off. I had heard "You hold on to that horse and don't fall off" so often that I held onto the reins and saddle and squeezed her sides with my legs with all my might. This was one time that I really felt afraid, but I never let my parents know. Before the summer was over, I was allowed to ride the two miles on the gravel road to my best friend Sarah's house. Her older sister Ouida rode Patsy but I thought her brother Orville was too big. I don't think Sarah was ever brave enough to ride her.

Though we only lived about three miles from town, it seemed like thirty. We had no phone and I felt cut off from my friends who lived in town, so Patsy helped me fill many lonely hours. When I rode through the pasture and up and down the shady lanes around the place where we lived, even up by the colored folks' cemetery and church, Dale Evans and Buttermilk rode with me. Sometimes, even Roy Rogers and Trigger would accompany us, and we all would sing the songs they sang in the Saturday movies. I knew the words to all their songs as well as the ones the Sons of the Pioneers sang.

School started in September, so I didn't ride Patsy very much, and then it was winter, wet and cold, and I didn't ride at all. We had a man, Old Gus, or Uncle Gus I called him, who helped around the place and would put hay out for Patsy and the cows. When I did come home from school and wanted to ride, he'd whistle her up from the back pasture and help me put a bridle and saddle on her.

One spring day I was sitting in class, looking out the window at how nice it was outside, and thinking how much I'd like to be out riding Patsy since I hadn't ridden all winter. When I got off the school bus, I changed clothes and headed outside to call her from the pasture. Now Patsy was always frisky and independent and not always ready to wear a saddle and be ridden. I had often seen Uncle Gus put a little feed in a bucket, whistle for her, and when she put her head in the bucket to eat, he'd slip the bridle over her nose and head. I looked around for Uncle Gus but didn't see him anywhere. I decided I could get Patsy bridled by myself. I got the bucket, and darn! We were out of feed! Oh well, I'd seen Uncle Gus fool her at times, too, so I got the empty bucket, went into the pasture to where the flat feed troughs were and called her. Up she trotted, ready to eat! She stuck her head in the bucket, and...

The next thing I remember was crippled old Uncle Gus holding me in his arms, hobbling as fast as he could into the house, hollering for my grandmother.

"Ms. Neal, Ms. Neal, dat crazy hoss done kicked Lil' Sis." About that time Daddy and Mother drove up from town where they had been grocery shopping and, ironically, bought feed for the horses and cows. Again, Uncle Gus shouted, "Mr. Mitch, dat crazy hoss done knocked Lil' Sis under da feed trough." As always, Daddy panicked and wanted to take me to the hospital, or at least go use the Lippencotts' phone and call Dr. Ellis, but Mother, always the cool-headed one, checked me over, put a cold washrag on my head, and said I'd be all right. I had the complete print of a horse hoof on my thigh and a knot on the top of my head where I was knocked under the feed trough.

The next day when I got off the school bus, there was a shiny, new blue bicycle at the house but no Patsy in the pasture. Daddy was sure if I hadn't been knocked under the feed trough, I would have been trampled to death. I was convinced the accident was my fault because I made Patsy mad when I tried to trick her with an empty feed bucket. The purchase of the bicycle was a complete waste of money because all the roads around, even our drive way, was gravel. Besides losing Patsy, I lost my friends, Dale Evans and Roy Rogers. Who ever heard of singing songs about the Western prairies while riding bicycles! To add insult to injury, Daddy had sold Patsy to Mr. Steadman, and my school bus went by his house and pastures. Each morning I would see Patsy grazing in the pasture. Mr. Steadman didn't have any children to ride her, so I knew she missed me.

I guess I never quite forgave Daddy for selling her with such haste, but that was his personality: do what you want to do quickly before anyone can change your mind. And now I realize that was just another time my dad told me that he loved me without using the words.

# Brickyard Hill

by Claire Feild

Daddy's Nash Rambler, looking like a small loaf
of Colonial Bread found in country stores in the fifties,
begins its workout, its shock absorbers doing push-ups,
those pulsating rhythms,
rhythms that abruptly stop, when the summit, a put-on
for a mountain, reveals itself.
Rows of shanties, humpbacks on each side of the road,
lend their dusk to the giant yellow sunflowers
crisscrossing dusty yards,
the sunflowers, unapproachable beanstalks for jacks of
no trades.
Black children, like jackstraws, fall in a heap before the
sunflower gods.
One child quietly escapes without disturbing the rest.

# Surprise Me on a Southern Night

## by Stephen Gresham

Emily stopped her car when she saw the pirate.

Or rather an old man standing in the middle of the road staring up at the street sign, disoriented, who wore pirate garb: a floppy hat, eye patch, and handlebar moustache; he even sported a steely hook and a peg leg.

Emily had been called in to substitute at work that evening. Jessie Lynn had not shown up. Again.

"You a real pirate?" said Emily.

The old man met her grin.

"No, just real lost." He told her he was going to a surprise birthday party for his grandson. "He loves pirates. All things pirate." A sad anger appeared to grip him. "I've been to his house many times. Dang it all—it's frustrating at my age not to find what you're looking for."

She liked him, this stranger, invited him to get in so that she could drive slowly along the street to jog his memory. She introduced herself; she didn't quite catch his name; he was simply an old pirate who pressed his face against the passenger side window and looked into the partial darkness with such hopefulness that she cringed.

"Can we call someone?" she said.

"No, please, I'll find it if I keep looking."

She decided to tell him about her job, how she hated it. "One night," she said, "this drunk student—I mean, totally wasted—he threw up right on top of his waffles. That did it for me."

"Wait," said the old pirate, "I think it's the next one." He peered. Shook his head, his body seized by disappointment. "No, no. Please stop the car. I need to get out and think."

As they walked along, she told him about Larry Don, the cook, recently divorced, who was always trying to get her to "hold my piece," a small revolver. "Squeeze it off—it's not loaded, girla." And the new waiter, J.T., a sex offender on parole—did something to a fourteen-year-old girl. Wouldn't say what.

She told him that she was living with a guy, Colin, who insisted that she hold a job.

"I don't think we love each other enough," she said.

The old pirate hesitated in his ongoing search.

"How much is enough?" he said.

"I don't know what I'm looking for in life," she said.

But the pirate did.

"There it is—that's where my grandson lives—thanks for your help."

All the houses looked the same to Emily.

She had been at work nearly an hour. No business. J.T., restless, was filling the sugar containers and dusting the counter with his shaky aim, then licking up the errant granules with a tongue that seemed much too long. Larry Don, bored to tears, played with his shiny, serpentine revolver and started in. Emily, waffle batter sticking to her new work shoes, grabbed the gun away from him just to shut him up. He grinned.

"How's it feel? Nice, right?"

Surprisingly, it did.

"Aim it," he said. "Aim it at the clock on that wall over there. Squeeze it off, girla."

She did.

A lovely, satisfying click.

"Swing it around," he said. "Do it again."

She did.

There was a sharp pop like a firecracker.

Everything instantly two-dimensional. Unreal.

Blood like too much ketchup on plain white bread, a many-angled round of stain morphing above Larry Don's heart. He crumpled, leaning against the wall as if exhausted. His heavy-lidded eyes were fixed at Emily's feet as if looking there intensely would explain something.

She was speechless.

At her shoulder, J.T., trembling, his bones rattling: "Holy cripes—why'd you do that?"

Turning into his face, not seeing him: "He told me to," she said.

J.T. quaking. "I ain't stayin' around on this. I can't get in no trouble, don'cha see?"

And he was gone. Didn't even take off his apron or visor. Vanished in the parking lot.

Emily watched Larry Don die.

It was as if his upper body slumped over just the way her large doll used to at one of her imaginary tea parties when she was a child.

What to do? Call 911. Then call Colin—no, he would be busy, and he would ask questions she could not answer. "You did what? My God, what were you thinking, Emily? Christ o'mighty! Who's going to save you on this? Christ o' mighty!"

She made no calls. She left the empty restaurant. She instinctively drove to the block where the old pirate had found his grandson's house. She smiled at the thought of the surprise party. Life should be filled with surprises. Good ones.

But when she reached the house, the old pirate was standing on the sidewalk staring up at a porch light he obviously didn't recognize. It was the saddest sight she had ever seen. When he heard the rush of her steps, he turned and said, "What are we going to do now?"

A surge of hopefulness burned in her chest.

"Keep looking?" she offered.

But the naivety of her words made her feel childish.

"No," said the old pirate, "no, it's time to stop." He rubbed his hook wearily against his forehead.

Emily was surprised to find Larry Don's revolver in her apron pocket; it was an alien, dark thing that should never belong in her world, and yet there it was. It diminished her.

In a little girl's voice, she said, "Are you going to tell on me?"

"For what?" said the old pirate, frowning.

Then she felt older again. Herself.

"For leaving my life behind." She paused. She wanted to throw the gun away, and she wondered why language failed when you needed it the most. "Everybody else is."

"No, I won't tell." The old pirate teetered on his peg leg as if about to fall. "But we need to find somebody to help us."

"OK," said Emily. She was fighting back tears of fright and confusion, and it had something to do with unintentional violence and more to do with surprises and how things truly exist. "OK," she said again. "Do you know the way?"

# Arab Tents of Saugahatchee Creek
## by Carol Lee Hartwig

The tents of Arabian nights, Egyptian haunts on the Nile, tribal villages along the Amazon...we lived and played in these venues along Saugahatchee Creek, a mile from Toomer's Corner in Auburn, Alabama.

The tents still stand where the bulldozers have not gone, the bends in the "Crick" still expose limestone for stepping stones and the crawdads still surely stealthily swim and walk. Cardinals, titmice, and mockingbirds still sing their incessant songs. The tents have soft pine needle floors. The walls are shrub trunks. The roofs an intricate canopy of honeysuckle vines springing green over a bower of golden fallen loblolly and long-leaf pine needles and oak-gum-cottonwood leaves.

The tents form intricate networks connected by a lacework of wisteria and kudzu vines that join massive trunks of oak, sweetgum, tulip poplar, and smaller trunks of chinaberry, iron wood, magnolia, and redbud growing along the banks of the Saugahatchee. Young slim bodies could crouch and wriggle through the branches and sit cross-legged on the pine needles. I felt protected and secure. We would talk about where we would sleep, which tent would be ours, and where the food would be cooked. I brought jar lids and arranged these plates for a family of twenty-one, I might one day have.

My older sister showed me how to get out of our bedroom window early in the morning before our parents arose: quietly open the roll-out window all the way, remove the screen, slide sideways until with dangling bare feet you hit the wet grass. "We're in Brazil," she hissed in my ear, her spittle and hot breath suffocating and exciting, pulling me toward the Creek as we struggled to stifle our giggles. We scampered across the neighbors' yard, no fences, and for us as children, no boundary, no divide, no surveyed property lines existed. Now we had just to rouse our two playmates on either side to make our band four. And then six, once the other two were born and carried about the yard for years until they could also join in. The three yards were as if one, and surrounded as we were by wild forest land on three sides, we roamed, hiked, and explored but the creek was our main passageway.

Our entrance to the creek began at the bridge on our driveway, a central gathering place for adults, children, and animals—and overlooking the largest pond. One morning there was a four-inch crayfish, playing statue as we rushed forward to see it. The menacing creature stood high on its appendages, pincers at the ready like a boxer, not twitching or waving, just stock still until we scuttled off to bring others. Upon our return, it was gone as silently and stealthily as it had appeared. What mysteries these events were. One dawn, there were two water snakes curled together at the waterfall from the culvert under the bridge, the sound of the falling water masking our voices. They were so comfortable, wrapped together atop a root shelf at the edge of where the water splashed and foamed. We smiled at each other, the four of us.

Vicious warfare occurred on the Nile. Snapping turtles, their plated backs locked in battle one windy cloudy day. One humongous head the size of my father's fist with a hooked snout that viciously grabbed and held his smaller opponent, the two of them splashing round and round until one in humiliating defeat swam away to the depths of the pond.

Across the street, where the creek meandered, there was an African savannah where a fox was spotted hunting amongst the tall grasses. The youngest of our tribe discovered a burdock with large round seed heads with hooked spines. Ever our leader, my older sister experimented with pulling back and tucking in her long hair using the seeds to secure this fancy hairdo. Excited hair styling ensued and triumphantly we four traipsed across to show our parents. The evening was spent with our heads in our parents' laps as they applied painful brushing, combing, and untangling. Their gasps and moans at the hairy-spiny tangles were matched by our howls and protestations, after which we were instructed not to try that again.

The trips down the Amazon were the best fun, far away from our homes. We took a lunch, we were barefoot all day, and we whistled, squealed, and shouted. The cool creek had a sandy bottom that changed to gray clay in places. We made pottery, hunched over, squatting along the creek's edge, leaving the pots to dry on a rock. We discovered tributaries; we named an island "Crow Tree Island" for obvious reasons. At a bend in the creek we found a back channel and in that short muddy pond with sloping banks there was quicksand. Quicksand provided abundant fuel for our young imaginations. We took turns letting the slimy muck suck us down to our waists until laughing and screaming "quicksand" we pulled each other onto the bank. Many trips were made back to relive that safari, Hollywood style, complete with mock surprise falls into the quicksand, frantic struggles, and finally last-minute triumphant rescues.

The rewards of living on Saugahatchee Creek were bitter-sweet. The creek had a heavy aroma on summer days, the water turned red and brown and there were floods that brought the levels over the bridge during hurricane season. In disgust, my father claimed that new parking lots and subdivisions were causing more water to flow into the creek and that City Hall used our creek like a storm sewer. Cary Woods School was built farther down the creek. One day in fourth grade, our teacher decided to show us how to plant a garden with a new fangled seed tape. She needed some peat moss and our Creek tribe convinced her that we could gather peat moss at the creek. While nervous about unleashing us, yet in need of the peat moss, Mrs. Taylor let us loose. The class went wild, we ran through the woods down to the Creek, some kids fell in with their good clothes, we picked and poked at the slimy green moss on the rocks, laughed and wondered if this was truly peat moss, dragged it in small bits back up the hill to the school and flung it at our teacher's feet in the trench she had made. There were severe repercussions for that misunderstanding; peat moss was brown not green we were told many times thereafter as we were made to clean up and the seed tape was never mentioned again, the experiment in gardening dropped.

But we were not dissuaded from our early morning trips, not even by the two copperheads killed by a man with a long staff after my mother and I stepped next to the happily curled snakes on our way to cut marshmallow sticks for Girl Scouts. The danger just heightened the allure and we dragged visiting cousins or friends down the creek in search of adventure. Even after becoming half civilized, we continued to hunt the wildlife, wade the waters, and search for new tent encampments. After these forays when our feet were covered in creek silt and ooze and our clothes and hair covered in needles and leaves, fresh scratches on our legs and arms, we hungry savages craved treats. My sister knew what to do, she stole the family dark green ceramic sugar bowl with Cuban sugar, a knife right from the cupboard, and a Mediterranean lemon. Cutting slices of lemon, dipping them in sugar, she showed us the ultimate reward: we sucked the sweet, sour juice, the sensation contorting our mouths and bodies into cringing and exploding gyrations and then laughter. The wild and wonderful Saugahatchee, our passageway to experience the world!!

[Saugahatchee Creek is seventy miles long. The Creek Indian name, "Saugahatchee" means "rattling river." Saugahatchee Creek is one of the largest creeks in the Lower Tallapoosa Sub-basin (of the Alabama-Coosa-Tallapoosa Basin which is part of the Mobile Basin) at two hundred and twenty square miles.]

# Dirty Laundry
## by William Ogden Haynes

Without a washing machine,
she had plenty of time
to talk to the laundry
in the spring of 1950.
Behind the old shotgun house,
she worked in the back yard
with galvanized tubs, wicker baskets
and three clotheslines strung
on rusty metal poles
stuck in the dusty red Alabama clay.
"I hate you," she told her husband's work shirt
as she drowned it in the soapy water
giving it an extra squeeze for good measure.
Wringing out her son's underwear
She said, "Don't you be growin' up like him."
She pinched a clothespin on the hem
of her daughter's green cotton dress and warned,
"Be careful who you marry, girl."
She stared at the clothespins sitting on the line,
examining her, as a murder of crows on a telephone wire
look at a wounded possum on the side of the road.
She startled when the damp wash on the clotheslines
snapped like flags in a gust of warm wind,
reminding her of slaps
and slamming doors.

# Finding Bones

by Peter Huggins

I am always finding bones
In the woods behind my house,
Mosasaurs or zeuglodons,
A paleontologist's dream.

The neighborhood children use
These woods for games and exploration.
I see them running past.
Sometimes they stop and share

My fascination with bones
As I unearth eighty
Million years of the past
From one bit of Alabama.

The older children
Avert their eyes.
They trudge down the path
To the fifty-foot drop

Or to the hut they built
From odd pieces of lumber
Or fallen wood they picked up
After last week's storm.

I am not prepared then
For what comes from my dig
Early one morning—
Love cries, soft moans, a giggle.

As you might imagine,
My appearance startles them.
They stop in mid-stroke, uncouple,
Grab their clothes, and run.

The wonder of that act
Leaves an afterglow
In the burned air
That surrounds this site.

I get my brushes and brooms.
I dig down
Toward mythic discovery,
Femur, thigh, rib,

Claw, skull, and spine.
I swear I'll piece together
One whole skeleton
Before I am through.

# At the End of the Road, A Graveyard

by Bailey Jones

Though they appear to mean the same thing, some words should be defined differently. Take, for example, "graveyard" and "cemetery." To me, the mental image conjured by the word "cemetery" is one of neat rows of tombstones, set in freshly mowed grass. The majority of the dates carved in the polished marble are from this century, even some from this year.

A "graveyard," however, has an air of neglect, the result of disuse and isolation. Gnarled old trees surround the site, with weeds and younger trees struggling for space between the graves, none of which is new. Large black crows often perch on nearby branches or even the gravestones themselves, keeping a careful eye on those who might pass. Nature is the caretaker in a graveyard.

Just up the road from the lake cabin that was my childhood summer home was a graveyard. The randomly placed crumbling tombstones, twisted trees, choking weeds, and my overactive imagination combined to create a wonderfully eerie atmosphere. A mummy could walk through this graveyard and feel right at home. Best of all, several of the graves were covered by raised slabs of stone, as if no hole had been dug for the dead; they had been placed on the ground and covered by a stone casket. And some of these caskets had been broken. But had they been broken from the outside, by grave-robbing marauders, or the ravages of time? Or had they been broken from the inside, by… well, who knows? And did it matter?

Walking to the graveyard was an important part of summer when I was growing up. It was one of those things that you just did, like eating every ripe blackberry you found, right off the vine. The walk was only a mile-and-a-half up the dirt road, but when you're seven years old you have to take a lot of steps to go a mile-and-a-half. If it was dark, they were very tentative steps. You strained your ears and eyes, listening and looking for the monsters and vampires that were lurking out there somewhere, just waiting . . .

I walked to the graveyard probably a hundred times before my seventh summer, always at night and never alone. I understood the phrase "there is safety in numbers" long before I ever heard it.

After dinner, all of the kids at the cabin (there were always quite a few of us) would gather up all the working flashlights we could find. The usual ratio was one light per three kids, and, if we were lucky, a book of matches "just in case." (This was before the days of the Bic lighter and the adults tended to hold onto their matches. I think the thought of scared little kids running amuck in the woods, armed only with matches, scared them a little. Looking back, it scares me a lot.)

The first part of the walk was more like a long-range frog-hunt than an adventure into terror. It wasn't until the last half-mile or so, when we realized exactly what we were walking towards, that the first icy fingers of fright began to tickle our spines. But we always pressed on.

The last hundred yards were the worst. The graveyard was at the bottom of a small hill, and the trees grew larger and thicker along this part of the road. Their long branches stretched over the road like a skeleton's fingers grasping for a young victim. What little moonlight there was got swallowed before it could break through the branches. Looking down that last stretch of dirt road was like looking into a dark tunnel of terror. We knew something waited for us in that cloak of darkness, something we had no desire to meet.

More terrifying than the denizens of darkness were the painful taunts reserved for the cowardly, so we never turned back. We went into the tunnel, shining our flashlights every which way at once, their pitiful beams showing nothing except more darkness ahead. We walked quietly and held our breaths, listening for the footsteps of whatever was waiting for us in the woods, but these monsters were clever. They walked silently, and just out of range of our flashlights.

After an eternity, we would see the graveyard. The tilted tombstones looked like hungry zombies who just spied a meal, but we didn't care; it was comforting to know that we'd completed our journey.

For some reason, walking to the graveyard was a lot scarier than walking through it. We would wind our way through the scattering of tombstones, reading aloud the century-old dates and the inscriptions that never changed, yet remained fascinating:

> "Sleep little Andrew;
> Not in your cradle bed,
> Not in your mother's arms;
> But with the sacred dead."

By the time we meandered to the back of the graveyard, where the graves were so old that time had erased the dates and inscriptions, whoever was following us was ready to scare the wits out of us. We always knew they were coming, but we got scared anyway. Even if we recognized Uncle Bob or Cousin Tom right away, we were at least one hundred yards down the road before we could convince our legs that there was no danger. By then the fright would be over, and we had an adult to escort us back to the cabin. Not that we needed one, of course.

There was one trip that stands out from all the graveyard walks we made. There were about fifteen of us that night, most between the ages of seven and nine; it was Family Reunion Week, and we were ripe for a fright.

The walk to the graveyard was no more eventful than usual. It wasn't until we reached the back of the graveyard that I had the eerie feeling of being watched.

I shone my light on, around, and behind the old graves—nothing. I scanned the edge of the woods, looking for the evil red eyes that I could feel boring into my soul—still nothing. I looked behind the trees, and then I looked up into the branches. In one of them I saw a ghost.

I tried to scream, but I couldn't find my voice. My legs also had a mind of their own, and when they turned to run I willingly followed. Unfortunately, they carried me by one of the open graves. A rotting corpse rose from it and the scream finally escaped my throat, but no one else heard me because they were all screaming and running, too.

Somehow, we all made it home alive. Somewhere along the road I had stepped in a bed of fire ants, but I didn't even notice until I had run the entire mile-and-a-half home—in just under six seconds, and as usual in foot races, I trailed the pack.

I realized then that the ghost looked a lot like my cousin Steve would look if he had draped a sheet over his head. And the rotting corpse had borne a strong resemblance to my mother.

Several years later, I forgave them.

Today, I realize that because of that night I am able to live alone, "out in the middle of nowhere." I'm in the woods and on a lake. If this were a *Friday the Thirteenth* movie, I would be killed before the opening credits rolled.

Now, when I'm reading a Stephen King novel and the lights go out or I'm sitting on the dock and notice that the woods have grown quiet—too quiet—I think back to the night I saw my mother rising from an open grave in a graveyard that would frighten Frankenstein. What could be scarier than that?

# A Selection From
## *A Cry of Absence*
### by Madison Jones

When Hester was a very young child she had imagined that the Lord had laid it out with His own hand—the patterned garden beside the house, the orchard behind, a fence here, and there a swooping meadow half shady with water oaks. Down the incline toward the gate, as it had done from the beginning, the drive divided itself to pass around the first and greatest of pecan trees. Boxwood balanced boxwood along the front walk and twin urns stood like counterweights at ends of the broad porch step. Who but the Lord could have raised those columns up—and so long ago that the big crossbeam now faintly sagged in the intervals between them? For all his antiquity and his looking, with clipped beard and smoky eyes, a little as the Lord must look, her grandfather was not even born in that far-off time. She thought that nobody was born then. When God made the house and set down in their places behind it the barn and the smokehouse and the four log cabins across the field in a stand of chinaberry trees, there was not a sound in all the world. Then he made birds and chickens and cows, so that when he made people the sounds were already here, whistling and crowing and bawling in the fields. Then he made people: the white ones first, to live in the house, and then the black ones, to feed the stock and farm the cotton that the white people showed them how to plant. It was all exactly as His hand, in that original silence back at the beginning, had made it to be.

Summer days at Fountain Inn seemed in her memory all one endless day, beginning with roosters. High up in the house she waked to their shrill voices streaming like the banners of sunrise through her tall window. And soon, the bell, its silver resonance soaring over the fields. There were other sounds—thuds and clink of harness, Negro voices wordless and mellow like echoes in a drum, someone calling.

There were so many sounds of morning. She could hear Ben's ax at the woodpile and the slow creak of the well pulley. At the barn was a tingling or rasping of milk in a tin pail, and a crunching of corn in big mules' teeth behind the shut stall doors. From the cabins out in the field came the cries of colored children playing. She would be there soon, with Link and Annie and Della May, all on their knees in the deep dust at the shady side of a cabin. "You be de princess, I be de knight." Around them in the fields and the chinaberry trees was the crying of locusts and meadowlarks. The afternoon droned and clucked with chickens. Old Burtie stumped about the kitchen or ironed on the back veranda where Hester lay on her belly, bare feet against the rail, and listened to inexhaustible tales of Burtie's wonderful life. The high parlor was cool, always. Her grandmother sat here, darning or sewing with wrinkled, miraculous hands, tall and straight in her walnut chair, and told about Hester's father when he was a little boy. About other things, too, old things, in a time that she said was different from this. There had been the War, she said. Before it, there had been a life they would never see again. But Hester doubted. She knew that it had been a real war. Over the mantel hung the shining cavalry sword that her grandfather had used in it. But how had the war been lost, for where was the difference it had made? The life of which her grandmother spoke seemed faraway only in time, and that sword looked as bright and flawless as any victor's sword. And the tales of glory she had heard, of Lee and Forrest and Jackson? Whatever was lost seemed sad to her only because they had lived so long ago.

It was being old, Hester thought, that made her grandfather sad. His hands trembled upon pages of the Bible and other books he read, and sometimes, when he turned around, the gaze resting upon her would make her think of filmy smoke in the hollows of his eyeballs. But then he would smile and, if she was close enough, put a dry hand on her head. Most afternoons he sat in the summerhouse by the fountain, reading through silver-rimmed glasses that straddled the peak in the ridge of his nose. At times he would read aloud to her, about Abraham and Moses and the children of Israel. His voice was younger than the rest of him. It still came to her memory fused with a gentle splashing from the fountain outside, where the mouths of four little angels sprayed water into the circular basin around them—cold water, spewed up from deep in the earth. Picking and chewing at stems and leaves that grew in through the lattice, she listened and thought of the children wandering in the desert. The desert lay beyond the ridge where she had never gone. Right here was what they had been seeking—this green land where the fountain flowed.

Somehow Fountain Inn had seemed always to be at the center of Hester's childhood. In fact this was not so. The weeks and summers spent there barely counted against the years at her home on Hampton Street. Nor did the figures of her grandparents compete in her mind with those of her mother and father.

Still there was a way in which Fountain Inn seemed more her home than this, as if she had lived there a dimly remembered primal life before this present one had dawned. And it was true, in a much more reasonable way, that this life here on Hampton Street did derive from that one. Her father did, and the house itself, so many years ago.

And so, in a lesser way, did the life of the town, for Hester. For one thing, there was its history, which she knew even in childhood—how the name and the land both were the gift of her great-grandfather Cameron. It was only natural that her father had been the mayor more than once, and that, until his last years, he had been one of the powers to say what would and would not be in the town. There were other powers, of course, names like Traynor and Willingham and Qualls, which she recognized. To her, these were names of lesser magnitude, but they too, she imagined, had come from places almost like Fountain Inn. In her more contemplative moments she saw that not only her house and its people but the whole town was like a birth from this primeval source. The town also, for all its differences, had its dusty roads down which the cotton wagons rattled, its quiet old houses in droning summer heat, its Negro cabins in deep backyards, and women in head rags and black children in hearing distance. The fields were not far. Milk cows driven by Negro boys passed by her house at morning and evening, and, in the season, murmurous gangs of men and boys with cotton hoes swinging and glancing over their shoulders. Lucinda in her kitchen was a younger Burtie, with tales not much less wonderful. And Poss, in her yard, was as old as Will. Hester was not sure which ones among the white people were her real kin. There were so many she called by the name of Uncle or Aunt or Cousin, whose houses she could enter as she entered her own. There was not any house, white or Negro, whose people she did not know at least by name, and no event or change of scenery that had for long escaped her notice. There were differences enough from Fountain Inn, all right, but underneath it all was the pattern that the Lord's hand had shaped.

This was how the world was, she thought, and changes were no more than the wrinkles and passing tumults that wind could raise upon the face of things. She never had forgot the first occasion when this ground seemed to quake beneath her feet. Old Dr. Phillips, the Presbyterian minister, was much in her house, for meals and for sick calls, a stern, ascetic man with gray moustache and a voice that was habitually a little louder than other people's. He did not look so much like the Lord as her grandfather did, but Dr. Phillips's sudden death, when it came, was like the most vivid of challenges to every right and permanent thing. Righteousness itself seemed threatened. If such things happened, why not to drunk Bob Wakefield, who went on staggering about the streets? But still the shock was in no way equal to that she felt a year or so later when she saw her grandfather lying like a figure of wax in his coffin.

In a little time, of course, her wounds healed over. And probably these were among the things that had prepared her not to be so conscious yet of her father's distress at what was beginning to happen in the town. It was something, he said, that had come in with the motorcar, and the noise and the dust they raised on the unpaved streets. She could see the motorcars, all right, though there were not yet so many of them; and, with his opinions in her mind, she imagined that she could perceive something of the new spirit that he was always describing in words like "aggressive" and "licentious" and sometimes even "wicked." But Hester's mind was so busy elsewhere, then. Already, at thirteen, she was in love with Thomas Glenn.

It had happened, she always remembered, on Confederate Memorial Day. There was the usual parade of creakily animated veterans in their faded uniforms marching four abreast around the square, with dust and banners and rebounding strains of "Dixie" and "The Bonnie Blue Flag" that excited the flesh like wind from distant battlefields. She saw him all at once, as in a burst of light. Among the spectators were many men on horseback, but he, he and his sorrel mare, stood literally heads and shoulders above the rest. It was because his horse had reared, reared and stood there. In her memory of it they never had come down. They were still poised there like a horse and rider just on the threshold of soaring into flight. Her beloved, too, was in uniform, full regalia that looked as if it had been made for him, and a shining saber was at his side. Standing straight in the stirrups, as tall as the horse, his golden head bare because the cavalry hat had fallen onto the back of his neck, he seemed to her as blinding bright as the sun in a morning sky. She was madly in love with him.

He was not as tall as he had looked then. In fact, as she discovered in later years, he was barely an inch taller than herself. From the distance at which she worshiped him, however, she thought he would have to stoop his head to walk through an ordinary door. But her love was a secret she kept very close: for years she never breathed a hint of it, not even to her mother. The reason, besides that of her childish modesty, was the reservation that she felt in her parents' attitude toward the Glenns. Certainly the Glenns were numbered among the people who counted and, in a way of speaking, they were friends of her parents. The friendship, however, was only of a kind based on mutual position and respect, and mainly was expressed by occasional visits to each other's homes on Sunday afternoons.

Probably no real intimacy had been possible between the two families. It was not a difference that had anything, or anything substantial, to do with class. Rather it had to do with temperament, and might have been epitomized, in that day, by the difference between the Episcopal and Presbyterian churches, to which, respectively, the Glenns and the Camerons belonged. On certain matters, they simply had irreconcilable attitudes. Hester's parents' reservations about the Glenns—which she had quite naturally sensed—were grounded largely on the feeling that the Glenns were of a kind deficient in full and appropriate moral earnestness. As for the Glenns' feelings, Hester was uncertain whether, behind a facade of perfect manners, they were not smiling at the abundance of this quality in her parents. Anyway, in her childhood, this thought, like thoughts of wickedness, was vaguely titillating to Hester and added to her fascination with Mr. Glenn. She had considered him to be the handsomest man who ever lived. With his confident posture and streaked gray beard, he was the image of the Confederate cavalry officer . . . And his son was like him, she thought later on.

No doubt it was what Hester felt in her parents' attitude toward the Glenns that invested Thomas with a certain indefinable air of the forbidden. This was what caused her not unpleasantly shuddering fancies of a dark and mysterious side to his character. But dare one ever marry such a man? Above all, her mother had told her many times, be sure of goodness and honor in the man you marry. Then worry about his other qualities. How, therefore, could she marry him?

Of course, in actuality, these girlish fantasies were based on nothing—or nothing except her sense of her parents' feelings. And these, a few years later, she saw for what they were, a matter not to be taken with any great seriousness. It came to this: the Glenns were rather worldly people. These, in fact, were her mother's very words when it became apparent, in Hester's nineteenth year that Thomas's courtship of her daughter might conceivably end in marriage. But as for their actual moral comportment, she knew nothing against them. It was, then, merely the matter of temperamental difference between the families, and Hester could have wished never to have been marked with even the inclination to suspect that more was behind her parents' feeling than now appeared. Because of it she had to make a certain effort in order to dismiss unpleasant rumors that sometimes reached her ears. Still, she was a woman now and no longer so ignorant where the ways of the world were concerned. She would not believe such rumors, but what if there was some truth in them? Young men away at the university, not yet bound by clear ties of honor, were often given to follies. That was the way of the world. To balk at this was prudery. By the time he proposed marriage to her, during her last year at the women's college at Blanton, her old reservations were nothing but memories infrequently recalled.

Yet, as she finally had seen, she would have done well to take warning from those prudish girlhood instincts. Had they not, perhaps, been premonitions, really? There was a kind of moral refinement that often, in certain realms, could sense an evil not yet even out of its germ. Her mother had had this quality, Hester thought, and maybe had passed it on to her daughter, in vain. But whatever the source of those feelings, they did appear prophetic at last. Indeed, on her honeymoon, even, for all the strange excitements of her flesh, she had experienced in Thomas's very knowing embraces a consciousness of old specters rising into her mind again. It was a last, late warning, and, as her body grew accustomed to such use, she had dismissed it.

Concerning Thomas, what would she not have dismissed in those earliest years of their marriage? Always attentive, with small gallantries and presents and inquiries after her comfort, he had left her in no doubt about his love. Nor had she any reason to doubt that what she saw reflected in those polished manners and fine, gray, responsive eyes was the real character of her husband. He was all she could have asked for. She was as proud as if he had been shaped in the very pattern of what a man ought to be.

# Circle of Houses
## by Gail Langley

*In the South, the August air has a sound that precedes fall, forecasting cooler weather. The cool does not come as promised for some time, although the calendar summer is ending. It's actually not a sound but the absence of sound, as if any noise required sifting through the heated air in order to be heard. Dogs will pause from a trot, lift and turn their heads while birds take flight from a wire only to return to their exact starting point. An electrical zap has charged the air with a pressing silence. The nights are not as soundless with the crickets chatting. Darkness comes late in the Alabama summers.*

The young college boy bided his time, waiting for the night shadows, only then walking into a small pine thicket behind the circle of houses. He propped his shotgun against a young loblolly pine and put his back to another. He could see each house. Six of them. One had a small garden not ten steps from the back door. At times, the smell of red dirt and blood red tomatoes would drift through the pine thicket where Toby kept vigil.

The quiet was unnerving, but Toby was already unnerved long before waiting for each house to go dark. He had a plan for the occupants… a plan born from some unfathomable thought from a brain that had broken. Braced against the small pine, he steadily watched the second house on the circle. Fireflies floated in such abundance that at times the little thicket became lighted by their syncopated glow. Still, Toby remained undetected. He was obsessing about the women in the house. How they'd taken his heart and put it in a dark place, so he could no longer feel a pulse or recognize his own mirrored face. His soul was wandering in a lost gray cavern of their making. Soon theirs would be as well.

Staring at the windows, he hoped to glimpse Katy or her mother. His love for them was causing this sickness. He could feel something fetid and green moving though his veins. Touching the knife on his belt reassured him of his strength… empowering him to cure himself.

As he waited, Toby thought about the time that he hit Katy, just once, and only because he loved her so much. As a result, police instructed Toby not to go near any family member. After that it took days just to breathe in a regular pattern.

He tried to go back to his studies, but found their names typed between each line of text. Katy, Roberta, Katy, Roberta, Katy, Roberta. They were smart women, mother and daughter. Both dark-eyed, porcelain skin. Not really beautiful, but strangely engaging, attracting him to this place of madness.

A screen door opened in the neighbor's house, and a lop-eared, blond, cocker spaniel bounced into the evening. Toby became alert as the puppy sniffed its way into the trees, zigzagging to some titillating pattern of scent. The dog did not bark, keeping the boy's secret. Eventually reaching Toby, the dog walked tentatively, retreating each time the boy reached out his hand. Soon, the spaniel joined the boy. Both sat quietly in wait. Not until Dr. Collins called into the night did the spaniel bound home, drawn by his master's voice.

Dr. Collins would be the first to witness the mayhem after Toby's rampage. Quietly slipping through a window, Katy would flee to the doctor's house. Vera Collins would summon the police while Dr. Collins took up his pistol instead of the black case he carried when responding to a panicked mother. This would be like no other house call.

This is a small village. The permanent residents can call each other by name and list most of the college students who abandon us in the summer. When in late August, Toby Stephens killed three young girls and wounded Mrs. Sims, we began locking our doors. Days after the murder, townspeople were repeating each newspaper fact trying to comprehend the slaughter of three innocent girls. We were not normally a cautious people, yet we began to travel in groups to and from the town bowling alley or city pool fearful for our own lives which were not so different from Katy Sims'.

Nevertheless, Katy's life was now different, altered by terror on an August night. She had survived Toby's frenzy, hiding in a broom closet until the sound of the killings had subsided. One other sister had survived. Toby, in his fervor, had not paused to look under the bed where the surviving sister was pressed to the hardwood floor afraid to take in a shallow breath. The two six-year-old girls were easy prey, abandoning their day in the deep sleep reserved for those who still count their age on their fingers. They clutched their dolls, in a dreaming mist, slumbering to their death. Toby shot the dolls as well as a sister asleep in the adjoining room.

Curiosity drove many to witness Toby's trial. I was not a voyeur to the gruesome details, and the parts I do know, I will not repeat here. I think of Toby Stephens, my classmate, in his school days perched on the science desk next to the arched faucet. We laughed behind our hands while Toby whistled the calls of each Alabama bird, a science project as strange as the boy. Amused at the thought of Toby stalking birds, our imaginations could not move beyond the world of wooden desks to a woods in an August evening behind a circle of houses.

# Whistler's Son
## by Terry C. Ley

My father had many talents. He built our house, for one thing, and he could administer first-aid successfully to almost anything mechanical, from our Ford coupe to my electric train. Unfortunately, I did not inherit any of those talents.

But Dad was also a whistler. He whistled unconsciously while he laid the cement blocks that formed our basement or drove my mother to the grocery store. He whistled loudly when it was time for me to come in from playing. He often whistled softly while filling out his "time sheets" each weeknight at the kitchen table so that John Deere would pay him on Friday. He could whistle by puckering his lips. He could whistle through his front teeth. By placing two fingers near his mouth, he could whistle so loudly that neighborhood dogs flocked to our yard. Sometimes I could identify the songs that he whistled, but often, I suspect, he was improvising.

I can't say that I admired his whistling then. Whistling was just another part of him that I took for granted. Some fathers could sing; some could recite poems. Mine whistled. A lot.

I seldom sought to imitate Dad's whistling. The only times that I remember attempting to whistle like he did were the times that I tried to whistle through my fingers. I failed repeatedly, and that was that. I still can't do it.

When I became a whistler I cannot say, but people began mentioning it when I was in my twenties. "You sound happy today," they would say—or they would ask, "What is that song that you're whistling?" Since others have brought it to my attention, I have caught myself whistling everywhere, at all times of the day or evening, while working at my desk, taking out the garbage, doing the laundry, even while vacuuming. Sometimes I cease whistling when I become aware that I am doing it, but in recent years I have just noted what song I'm whistling and wondered how that song flew into my head and out through my lips.

Sometimes I unconsciously take my cue from songs that I hear on the radio or on one of my CDs. Frequently I whistle all day Friday one of the anthems I have rehearsed with our church choir on Thursday evening. I sometimes whistle melodies from television commercials in spite of myself. Before entering a restaurant for lunch today, I heard a woman summon her friend in the parking lot.

Thirty seconds after she shouted "Laura!" I began whistling Laura's namesake tune. Most often, though, I cannot trace the immediate source of what I am whistling. During my half-hour walk through our neighborhood tonight, for instance, I found myself whistling "Walkin' My Baby Back Home" and "Peter Cottontail." For some reason, entering the shower seems to be my cue for whistling "How Long Has This Been Going On?" Usually I whistle very softly, to myself, but when I am in a jovial mood I sometimes turn up the volume. Others in the fitness center dressing room often hear me whistling loudly to celebrate the end of my workout.

I doubt that my whistling has much of a future, although I recently read about a young man from Virginia whose whistling has paid off. Chris Ullman has won four national and international whistling contests, whistled for the President, and whistled with the National Symphony Orchestra. He says he enjoys performing for an audience because whistling makes people happy. I can understand that. One day while browsing in a quaint bookstore in Montgomery, whistling softly, probably because I was surrounded by thousands of books, I was surprised when a gentleman touched me on the shoulder. I recognized him as one of the anchors for the nightly newscast that we always watched. "Excuse me," the celebrity said, "but I couldn't help hearing your whistling. Hearing someone whistle makes me happy. Not enough people whistle these days!"

I am convinced that whistling generally arises out of the whistler's happiness, too, that it is one way of expressing joy, spontaneously, privately or publicly. I am proud to be a whistler's son.

# Orange and Blue and Read All Through

by Lan Lipscomb

Three years ago, a collector in California offered me some papers that he had determined were originally in my family's possession and would be of interest to a family historian. These were mostly clippings, a letter, a photograph, and pamphlets—all treating my Lipscomb and Dowdell ancestors. I offered $150 and got my money's worth. Among the materials was a complete issue of the Alabama Polytechnic Institute student newspaper, *The Orange and Blue*, for March 27, 1901. A look at its four pages (a single sheet) reveals surprising details and gives interesting impressions about Auburn's town and campus one hundred and ten years ago.

In the years right after the turn of the twentieth century, the town of Auburn had a population of around one thousand and six hundred; the college claimed twenty-nine teachers and four hundred and twelve students, nine of whom were women. *The Orange and Blue* appeared every two weeks. It was not a "news" paper in our modern understanding of a publication that reports recent events of wide interest or importance. It was, rather, a five-column local interest publication covering both the town and school, filled with social, sports, and academic snippets; notices of campus and civic activities; witticisms and boosterisms; items copied from other papers; and local advertisements.

The nine headlines on page one read in order: "Athletic Advisory Board Meets. Elected J.D. Foy Manager Basket Ball and E.H. Wills Assistant Manager Foot Ball Team," "Dr. McIlhaney Visits the Y.M.C.A.," "A Friend of the Students Is Gone. Uncle Crawf Dowdell Passes Over the River," "Basket Ball Now an Inter-Collegiate Game With Auburn—J.D. Foy Elected Manager of the Team," "Baseball," "W.L. Noll Elected Captain of Track Team But Resigned," "The A.P.I. Cadet Band. One of the Best in the South," "Field Day: To Be a Meet of the Four Classes, Which Class Will Be Champion?," "Officers: Young Men's Christian Association for Next Year." Of these, the article on basketball may be the most significant in terms of the school's history, giving notice of development of the sport to the inter-collegiate level through an agreement to play the "Howard College Basket Ball Team . . . in

111

the Birmingham Athletic Club building on Friday night, April 12." A check of the 1901 yearbook reveals the outcome, the only game against another school's team: Howard 12, Auburn 7. David Housel, in his 2006 *Auburn Basketball Centennial*, dates the beginning of basketball at Auburn from five years later, January 19, 1906, when API defeated Tulane, 27 to 7, in the team's first year as a true varsity sport. In 1901 basketball was clearly a more informal enterprise, rather like a club sport.

A notice about baseball strikes a plaintively eloquent note. It was signed by the team manager Charles L. Harold who was looking at two games that coming weekend against Clemson College: "the season's hardest proposition." After commenting on the team's diligent practices, he remarks, "Now, what is the fundamental consideration is yet to be realized, the means to maintain and equip a respectable team. It seems that during the football season the students were sufficiently liberal to send out a truly representative football team, but upon the advent of the baseball season there is a marked decrease in spirit and interest and inevitably a corresponding diminution in readiness to contribute to the success of the season by giving dollars and cents." Only nine years after a game in Atlanta between Auburn and Georgia established intercollegiate football in the South, that sport was eclipsing the national pastime in interest and financial support. And much of that financial support, interestingly, for all sports in 1901 appears to have been through student subscription. The track team's newly elected but immediately resigning captain, W.L. Noll, fell under the influence of the preeminent sport, too. The article explained that he resigned "on account of having sprained an ankle during the football season." A cynic might remark that little has changed in the interim. Five of the nine notices on page one pertain to sports. No specifically academic matter appears on the front page.

Another front-page item praises the Cadet Band under bandmaster M. Thos. Fullan. It lists all twenty-five members and their instruments, explains that "often a student has to leave college as soon as he gets somewhat proficient on his instrument," and announces an upcoming free concert in Langdon Hall.

But the first-page article on "Uncle Crawf" Dowdell passing over the river is why this issue was preserved and came into my possession. The notice is for the death of my great-great-grandfather, William Crawford Dowdell. He had moved to Auburn in the early 1860s from nearby Oak Bowery and had been a trustee for the school from at least 1869 to 1879 when Auburn was known as the A & M College. William Crawford Dowdell was also the younger brother of James

Ferguson Dowdell, the second president of East Alabama Male College, as the school at Auburn was first known. Crawford Dowdell owned a large home on Opelika Road that boarded Auburn cadets, and he had been serving at the time of his death on March 17 in his sixth year as Auburn's postmaster. The bundle of papers including the student newspaper appears almost certainly to have been collected by his daughter, my great-grandmother Kate Dowdell Lipscomb. On her death, they probably went to her son Frank, and after he died in California in 1981 they eventually fell out of the family's possession. We learned from this article that Crawf Dowdell "was on the street Saturday evening, greeting the college boys and his other friends with his cordial smile and hearty hand shake, and when he retired Saturday night he seemed to be enjoying his usual health. Sunday morning he arose at his regular time, and while he was standing before the fire dressing he suddenly fell forward, when his wife, who was in the room, hurried to him. He was dead before she could reach him." Dowdell's death notice is the paper's only non-school-related article on the first page.

The first column of page two is the "masthead," a directory listing the paper's editorial staff. Below it are more notices and rosters for school and town institutions. API's seven fraternities (Alpha Tau Omega, Kappa Alpha, Phi Delta Theta, Sigma Alpha Epsilon, Sigma Nu, Pi Kappa Alpha, and Kappa Sigma) come next, followed by other college societies listed with their officers--including the Wirt and Websterian learned societies, athletic teams, and special interest clubs like that for bicycling. A notice indicates that the paper cost $1.00 per session, but a poem entitled "The Editor's Dream" implies that subscribers did not always pay up. The Post Publishing Co., Opelika, was the printer-publisher. The town's then four white churches—Methodist, Baptist, Episcopalian, and Presbyterian— are also listed in that order with pastors, other officers, and times of services. Demonstrating the close town and gown connection of that day, three of the four Sunday School superintendents were API faculty: Charles A. Cary (Presbyterian), John F. Duggar (Baptist), and Charles C. Thach (Methodist); Shel Toomer, an alumnus and local pharmacist, served the Episcopal church in that capacity.

Page two also has two articles that reflect the character of a school emphasizing science and mechanics but also of less exclusively local interest and more like newspapers as we know them today. One relates how Russian scientists, by measuring frequency of "involuntary closing of the eye [winking]," had proved that electric light [still a rarity in Auburn] was "least injurious to the eyes," when compared to candles, gaslight, and sunlight. Another describes "Prof. Wilkinson's

Invention."Levi W. Wilkinson of Tulane was an alumnus and former assistant in the A & M chemical lab who had developed a "new scheme . . . to give to the student, in picture form, a clear conception of the chemical changes taking place in any analytical process."

The school's female students and perhaps some young townswomen also get mention: "It is getting to be spring time now, and the birds are coming out to sing, the butterflies will soon be flitting around chased by the barefooted boy, and the summer girl is—sewing. Can't some of you boys—or girls—catch the inspiration of the season and contribute a few lines of poetry to the *Orange and Blue*?" The first coeds came to Auburn in 1892, and the newspaper suggests general acceptance by the overwhelmingly male student body in 1901. There may, however, have been some recalcitrance. An item, culled from a corresponding newspaper, was published "to show the boys what a girl can do." It reports track records made "at Vassar College, New York, by young ladies of that institution," including the 100-yard dash in 11 seconds; running high jump, 11 feet and 8 inches; standing broad jump, 6 feet and 11 ½ inches. The paper doesn't mention (as it went without saying) that the Vassar women competed in long skirts or the similarly voluminous and encumbering Bloomer costumes.

Some of the most detailed and wide-ranging information appears concisely in little more than one-half of the space on page three. Here, sixty "Brief Locals" or notices of one or two sentences treat sicknesses, visits, deaths, church-related matters, and faculty activities. The items mention three faculty members, nine cadets and one female student, three alumni, at least fifteen townspeople, and nearly twenty others—mostly visitors. Here's a sampling: "Cadet James H. Randle was called home on account of the death of his sister." "It's time now for the track team to get to work. There is unusually fine material for a track team this year." "Prof. C.C. Thach delivered a lecture on Lord Byron before the Girls' High School in Montgomery, a short time ago." "Cadet Claude Kauffman has been very ill with pneumonia, but he is recovering slowly, now." "Misses Smertt and Smith, of LaFayette, came down Saturday to see the college, but it rained so hard that they saw only the road between the depot and the hotel." "The Misses Wright were shopping in Opelika Monday." "Cadet Haigler has been very sick with the mumps. Cadet W.E. Finch is also afflicted with the fattening epidemic." "Mrs. James Smith, the daughter of Gov. W. J. Samford, was the visitor of Miss Mary Drake last week." "The students and Auburn people who remember Mr. Ramon Eraso will be saddened to hear that the young Venezuelan is dead. He was taken sick in New York, but reached his home in Caracas, Venezuela, before he died." Emma Bell Culver (one of ten API coeds, 1900-1901) is reported "very ill of late. We hope Miss Culver will soon be out again."

The lengthiest item in this section describes the newly renovated Methodist Church, now known as Founder's Chapel, on the corner of Magnolia Avenue and Gay Street. The original wooden frame structure was substantially modified and bricked in 1899; this notice treats just completed renovations to the interior: "beautifully painted" walls and "modernized and painted" seats to match "the beautiful and handsome pipe organ which was placed in several months ago." Pastor Brother Spain is commended as "a hustler" who "has done much toward building up his church in both a material and spiritual way."

One notice reveals grade anxiety: "Term examinations are now over and as a rule the outcome is somewhat gratifying. There were by far fewer IV's made during the second term than there were on the first." IV's were low marks, as two brief pieces of student poetry used as filler, reveal. The cleverer one reads: "Come gentle spring, / But do not bring / The wind that bangs the doors; / Nor 'xams, you know, / That make one go / Home on his all IV's."

One of the profoundest changes in one hundred and ten years of student journalism would have to be the quality of humor. There's plenty of it used as filler in the API *Orange and Blue*: "Mumps is 'all the rage' now. Many have no idea how 'swell' it is." "The 'Liquid Air' performance turned out to be all gas." "'Here comes a man I don't like,' said the banana peel on the sidewalk. 'I guess I'll give him the slip.'"

Leave it to Auburn's literary man to say something still clever and funny today. Robert Wilton Burton in an ad for his bookstore heads his appeal with what seems to be a bit of learned Latin for "I am and I can": "Sum et possum," but which is immediately undercut with "Some ate crow." The ad continues, "The latter were disappointed. They bought old junk that proved worthless. If they had exercised their reasoning faculties as they did their legs, they would have found the way to BURTON'S OLD BOOKSTORE, (twenty-nine years of age next February) . . . Books, Books, Books—all sorts of respectable books—well dressed books—sensible books—pleasant books—scientific and learned books. Drawing instruments and material strictly first-class at lowest prices. All shapes, sizes, and tints of fashionable Stationery. Commercial Stationery, Sundries. Cadets always welcome whether they buy or not."

T.A. Flanagan, in little notices sprinkled in the brief locals, advertised items such as "Hawes' $3.00 Hats, The latest styles"; he also used three larger ads, one showing the "Young Ladies' Favorite," a heeled dress-boot for $3. Flanagan's clothier competitors in Auburn who advertised were the Wright Bros. and W.B. Gullatte on Magnolia Street, as it was then known. Opelika clothiers in the paper were Lyons & Torbert, Greene & Dorsey, and Samford & Dowdell of S. Railroad St. An Opelika livery stable, owned by W.L. Carmack, advertised "Landaus, Carriages, Surreys and Buggies for Evening Drives, Party Calls and Marriages." Carmack's line of business was to be eclipsed soon enough by automobiles, but it was so prosperous in 1901 that his was the only advertisement to feature a phone number, "15," even though telephones wouldn't come to Auburn for another three years.

Shel Toomer and his stepfather B.D. Lazarus' drugstore has an unusual ad: "Inaugurations . . . Come high, but we must have them. When we went into business we inaugurated a policy which has been received with pleasure by parties of all political creeds—a policy of liberality in dealing, of selling goods for just what they are, of refunding money for unsatisfactory goods, of promptness and politeness [sic], and most important of all, accuracy in filling prescriptions." This talk of inauguration may be explained. At the time of this ad, Toomer and Lazarus had just moved into the building made available when their competitor R.H. Bragaw retired. They reestablished themselves in a location that eventually contributed the name "Toomer's Corner" to Auburn's most important non-university landmark. The ad touts its new location while assuring customers of maintaining its standards.

The Little Bonanza Barber Shop, Pomp Foster and Elijah Renfro proprietors, promotes in a small ad its clean towels and sharp razors and "Best of Service." "We solicit the patronage of college boys and guarantee our work to be best. Remember our place is next to Taylor's News Stand." By 1906, Mr. Renfro was in business by himself at the Orange and Blue barbershop, as Mickey Logue and Jack Simms's *Auburn: A Pictorial History* reveals. Logue and Simms write that Renfro was one of several African-American businessmen downtown and that he cut the hair of his white customers at his shop and black customers in his home. Another African-American businessman, the shoemaker William A. Colby advertises his "old stand next to Ward's market."

The school also advertised under its new name as of 1899, Alabama Polytechnic Institute, as well as the old, A & M College, in a notice signed by President William

Leroy Broun: "The courses of instruction include the Physical, Chemical, and Natural Sciences, with their applications; Agriculture, Mechanics, Astronomy, Mathematics, Civil and Electrical Engineering, Drawing, English, French, German and Latin Languages, History, Political Economy, Mental Science, Veterinary Science and Pharmacy." The notice then lists laboratory courses, location ("sixty miles east of Montgomery on the line of the Western Railroad"), boarding, and expenses. The latter two offer interesting details: "The College has no barracks or dormitories, and the students board with the families of the town of Auburn, and thus enjoy all the protecting and beneficial influences of the family circle." And more surprisingly, "There is no charge for tuition. Incidental fee per half session, $2.50; Library fee per half session, $1.00; Surgeon's fee per half session, $2.50; Board, per month, $9.50 to $15.00." Excluding board, the outlay for a term amounted to the same expense as one of Mr. Flanagan's pairs of shoes and a hat: $6. Some expenses, however, aren't mentioned: books, stationery, cadet uniforms, dues and subscriptions for supporting the various school organizations. Still, it seems that sending a son or daughter to API would have been an affordable undertaking for many families of that day.

Read *The Orange and Blue* of this long ago era, and experience a school and town remote from what we now know as Auburn and its university. But you get a sense of the place when it was still truly a village and its main institution was too small for dorms or for requiring tuition. You will detect that Auburn and the school shifted occasionally out of placidity and into vibrancy. There was a healthy town and gown inter-connection that came from civic and collegiate self-interestedness and pride. There was also inevitably some heartache for citizens and students. Death came quickly for the young and old. Negligible and almost forgotten illnesses today could be life-threatening then. But spring was in the air, and Auburn on that Wednesday in March 1901 seems through this window a place and time mainly of contentedness and simple pleasures.

# The Greeting Was Always "Christmas Gift!"

by Taylor Littleton

Years ago, in my pre-Auburn life, my mother and I always went shopping on the Saturday just after school let out for Christmas holiday, catching the Birmingham Electric Co. Streetcar at 78th Street for the long ride downtown. I would get ready for Mother's nod to ring the bell for the 20th Street stop as the car began its swaying climb over the viaduct, where often through the steam and smoke the red glow of a pig iron run from within the great furnaces was cast against the gray December sky.

I didn't know, of course, during that particular ride in the Christmas time of 1940 that within a week I would receive my most memorable childhood gift, a Western Flyer bicycle—which years later I learned came at the dear price of $18.50. Nor could I have known then that the fiery stream I could see from the window was a sign that the war, for America still a year away, was already in its implications ironically energizing the manufacturing power of the city and its slow recovery from the financial stresses of the Great Depression. Something of that recovery must have been implicit in the glitter and bustling vigor of the downtown view which opened up to the two of us as we walked northward toward its center. To a small boy thinking carefully about his few ten- to fifteen-cent allocations per friend, it was almost overwhelming as we passed through the enormous dazzling interiors of stores with names like Pizitz, Loveman's, Parisian's—around on Second Avenue, as I recall—the huge five-and-tens, Kress, Newberry's, and Woolworth's, where the first sound one heard on entering was the pleasant clattery of the long lunch counter.

And outside on the streets the lights of the movie houses—the Empire, Ritz, Strand, Alabama, Lyric—would begin flashing their signals in the fading afternoon light, adding to the splendor of the scene. Most of those places are gone now, finding in suburban malls throughout Alabama new names and even more magnificent forms of holiday decoration and ministry to our natural desire for gift-giving at this time of year.

I'm not sure just at what age memory—that is, the recollection of past

Christmases—begins to condition our expectation of that one approaching. Such recollections are essentially private, but photographs can initiate the linkage, and although picture-taking didn't routinely record the period of childhood holiday I'm describing, I'm glad each year when we are able to bring out the snapshot— together with the first tree ornaments my daughter made in kindergarten—which recalls the shopping trip with our own children twenty-five years later, this one to what must have been one of the first elegant suburban stores in the state, Loveman's at Montgomery's Normandale, where in his large chair on the second floor a Santa Claus with fatigue in his eyes still managed a cheerful smile for the three small boys in cold-weather jackets posing in his arms. That store too has gone the way of most of the others I've named, but I suspect all of them live still in the holiday imagination of thousands of Alabamians.

One further memory from those years, and one that in a sense brings all of this together—childhood and maturity, memory and expectation, the living and the dead—is a seasonal phrase used by my grandmother and her family. She lived at our house, had grown up in late nineteenth-century Alabama, and had her children there in the first two decades of the twentieth. Many of her family, her own children and her brothers and sisters, would come to visit during the holiday and their first greeting was always "Christmas gift!" That sounded old-fashioned to me since "merry" Christmas had firmly infiltrated my vocabulary and I couldn't understand the point of the phrase since those visitors weren't always bringing presents. It may be that the words had their origin in much earlier years in the life of her family when gifts themselves were uncommon and when those special ones at Christmas were less purchased than handmade, more highly personalized than those we usually give today. But I now think that the phrase, long since gone out of use, must also, be marked by loyalty, generosity, and gifts that unite the giver with the reassurance of quietly understood things privately shared with a few others. These forms of gentle reciprocity are indeed Christmas gifts, and are no more or less than acts of reclamation, resurrections of the spirit that may have been eroded during the long year and that needs new life for the uncertain winter days ahead, awaiting us no less in 2010 than in that distant American transitional year of 1940.

To be sure, there will always be in our obligatory experience gifts that are not Christmas ones in this sense, even though purchased at this time of year. But possibly those gifts we'll be seeking in the splendid malls and small shops in Auburn-Opelika, Montgomery, Atlanta we'll purchase for other reasons, perhaps those being suggested here. The great oppositions that seem especially fixed in our Christmas awareness are, for many of us, religious ones: those between Rome and Bethlehem, between Caesar's throne and the manger. But even in this season, though all of us must still live out the routine nature of our daily experience, we seem more than at any other time of year conscious in some mysterious revelatory way of the opposition in our secular perspective between the sterile claims of wealth and power and the defining humanity of our ordinary commitments and possibilities. And it is not at all sentimental, I think, to regard our shopping for Christmas gifts as an opportunity for our best self in its own small way to participate symbolically in our most enduring literary metaphor of this merry season: to reconcile the psychic distance between Ebenezer Scrooge and Bob Cratchit.

Whatever private associations are unlocked for any one of us by the advent of Christmas, for myself I hope that the gifts we'll buy for our little granddaughter and grandsons, for our children, family, and friends will give them pleasure and be what they may not have known they wanted to receive. And I'm certain, too, that just as on this cool November day, caught between memory and expectation, I'll recall more than once a scene from years ago in which my mother and grandmother would rise at the sound of holiday travelers entering the front hall and all calling out each to each, "Christmas gift! Christmas gift!"

# Letting in the Light
by Janet Mauney

We lived on the darkest road in Dewberry County when my grownup child, Joshua, came home from Birmingham and curled up in his bed like a wounded pup. Martha Gladys had left him, taking the furniture and all accessories, everything but his clothes, which were left in a pile on the closet floor because she needed the coat hangers. Joshua had a strong backbone, but he wouldn't talk. He wouldn't eat. It took a bite out of my heart, which has suffered many bites during my lifetime, some of which have never healed. I often suspect it has to work overtime to keep ticking normally. What could I do but try healing with fragrant foods and make the two young ones go outside to play?

The road was blocked from sunshine by towering water oak trees that sapped the moisture from the earth. Nothing grew around our house. We tried seeding grass and got only a ragged hemline out where the yard meets the road. Flowers and vegetables turned brown before they had a chance to show off the fruits of their maturity. My last effort had been tomatoes in large plastic buckets filled with sterilized, fertilized soil from Kmart. How could I go wrong? The vines grew pale green and serpentine, delicately curling around our back porch railings, little runners reaching out in all directions in their search for sunshine. Kind of like little snakes searching for a mother. No tomatoes.

Our road was named Klondike Road, like we were sitting on the Alaskan tundra, all but our little section which became known as Dark Road, even though it was really the tail end of Klondike, and nobody knew exactly where Klondike ended and Dark Road began. Close in toward town, Klondike houses had grass, flowering azaleas, daylilies, and daffodils, but at the two-mile line, the pavement stopped and the big oaks grew closer, their branches mingling overhead because strange vines wove back and forth and hovered over our house like a great domed nest. The air became murky and our yard was as dusty or muddy as the road, depending on the season. It was like living in a cave except not so damp and cool. By the time you got to our house, you knew you were on Dark Road, but you weren't sure how long you'd been there.

I had to drive over three hills at breakneck speed, dust flying out on both sides of my car, all the way to Pierce Landon's place before I found someone with an abundance of tomatoes to sell. "You're like a volcano, Artemis," he said, looking at the dust I had stirred up.

"That's me," I answered. "Lady Tornado!" He let me have half a bushel for half price, and I looked directly into his gray, gray eyes with the sprinkling of tiny gold sparks and said, "Thank you, Pierce. You never know, these may be just what my boy needs."

I tried to keep the sadness out of my voice, so Pierce wouldn't know how upset I was. He looked right back into my eyes and said, "You're welcome, Artemis. Anytime."

"You know Joshua's back?"

"I heard that," he said, and I wondered how. At that point, Joshua had only been home eleven hours and forty-five minutes and sleeping most of that. Dewberry is that kind of place. Not much to do except talk, but something twisted inside me every time people started in on us. Me and my three boys. I had enough on my shoulders without people talking and elaborating about us.

I cooked a tomato sauce with lots of celery, onions, and hot pepper, chopped fine, enough to jar anyone out of his senses, and plastered the French bread with butter and garlic. My feet grew tired from tracking up and down the hall to Joshua's room, bringing a tossed salad, laced with wine vinegar and oil, a heaping plate of spaghetti with my tomato sauce running over it in delicious rivulets, and a basket of hot French bread. He pecked at his food like a little sick chicken, and I longed to pet him, to console his pain, but I had to remind myself that he was twenty-one, a grown man who would be okay when he was ready. Meanwhile, he tormented himself with suspicions of another man in Martha Gladys's life. What might that man look like? How did he lure her away? What might they be doing together at this very moment? The worst sort of thinking. It never occurred to him that she might have left of her own accord, being a generally unhappy person who was too young to know her own heart.

The two young boys came home and ate like cannibals.

Some people think there are spirits on Dark Road, but I have no use for that kind of talk. It's been twelve years since I've lived out here and never once have I seen the hint of a ghost, unless you count the time my neighbor startled my heart by putting a neon 7-Up sign in the middle of his cornfield. Who was he trying to sell 7-Ups to, way out here in the middle of Dewberry? It took less than a week for the local boys to break out the lights. The rusty brown stem is still there, minus the 7. The Up points toward heaven, although it is readable only during daylight hours.

Even in the cemetery on the east side of town, where everything is greener, I've never seen a spirit, and I often go there at 3:00 a.m. when I can't sleep for worrying about whether my boys are okay growing up without a father. I talk to Sonny, my husband. I wasn't expecting him to die. When I left him at the hospital, his chest hurt, but he was in stable condition. I barely had time to get home to Dark Road and tell the children where their father was before they called me back.

At first, right after he went, I felt my heart might stop along with his. I used to kick his tombstone in anger and say things I wouldn't want to be held accountable for now, because he brought me to Alabama and Dark Road when I was only 18 and left me too soon with three half-grown kids. I wished his spirit would rise up, so we could duke it out then and there. The kicking hurt my feet, which have to be in good shape to stand in those high heeled shoes at the bank all day and tend to those boys at night, so I turned to wine, which is the only spirit I'm familiar with anyway. I broke the empty bottles over his gravestone, right where his head ought to be resting peacefully.

After four years, the anger is gone and I just talk things over with him. Quietly. Like, "Sonny, what in the world will I do if Joshua doesn't snap out of this?" I never get an answer, but it makes me feel better, and I knew Josh's heart would mend, but by the time I got ready to give my heart to Jesus, it would be as small and hard as a turkey gizzard, brown and curling at the edges. Jesus would not be able to recognize it for the tender thing it once was.

When I got home from work the next day, Pierce Landon was sitting in his truck in my driveway. I parked my car. "Hello, Pierce. Why are you sitting out here in the heat all by yourself? For heaven's sake, come on inside."

He stepped out and got a full bushel basket of tomatoes from the back of his car. "Just thought you might could use these. I had some to spare." He looked away. Tried to hide a smile. He wouldn't let me pay him, but he did stay for supper.

I washed my hands with Octagon soap and hot water. Money is filthy stuff. It can seep right through your skin and get into your bloodstream before you know it. I see it happen at the bank every day. There just isn't any other place for a woman to work in Dewberry County.

I cooked a tender chicken, opened two cans of Pillsbury biscuits, and sliced the red tomatoes, covering them with hot black pepper, enough so anybody would sit up and take notice. There was plenty of rice and brown gravy, too.

Josh nibbled his food alone back in his bedroom, listening to requiem music on the classical radio station, so soft I thought I was imagining it at first.

"Mama," he said, "I should've stayed home more at night."

"Nonsense. She knew you were a musician when she married you."

"That's not the point . . ." The room reverberated with gloom.

"Josh, there's cobwebs on your ceiling," I said, swiping one with a paper napkin.

Pierce sat at the kitchen table with me and the two young ones, eating like he'd never had a good meal in his life. He even cleaned up what Josh left behind. While the boys took their baths, we sat out on the front porch enjoying a glass of beer. The murmur of the children's voices floated from the bathroom window and mingled with the sounds and smells of the evening, wild onions in the pasture across the road, oak trees rustling with the coming of fall. Small dark bats zoomed from tree to tree. Pierce is a tall, work-hardened man with a full head of hair, and he's lived alone ever since I can remember. If he had a wife, she must have been gone one way or another. Nobody could stay hidden around here for long.

"If you took down some of those oak trees, Artemis, you could probably grow something in this yard," he said. I told him I would think about that, knowing full well it would cost more money than I'd ever have.

When he got up to leave, he shook my hand, then held it and looked at it like he'd never seen it before. He turned it over and said something about it being so clean, tracing his finger down my lifeline, acting like there was more to come, but in the end, he dropped my hand and left without saying a word. I almost made a grab for him, almost tackled him right there in the dirt yard, but I held back. I had never been unfaithful to Sonny, but I was pushing forty and everybody in my family lives to be ninety.

I went to sleep that night listening to jazz music from Josh's room. A good sign.

Josh wanted me to move to Birmingham and find cleaner work. He's a musician and has more nightclubs and country clubs than he can handle. Since he came home, his band buddies call every day saying come on, Josh, we need you, man. He plays the drums, and everybody knows the rhythm section is the foundation of a good band. Josh was still heavy into guilt and self-pity, but that's out of my control.

The cemetery is quiet and can be a sad place if you walk around a bit. Especially in the old part where there are lots of children. Not too far from Sonny, there are two little sisters named Mittie Lee and Mary Ellen. Mittie Lee lived to be eight years old and Mary Ellen died at four. Both went on the same day. January 15, 1903. An epidemic perhaps. The mother's grave is beside them. She lived until 1953. She was Sonny's great grandmother, and he said she never recovered.

How could she bear it? A burden like that. Her heart must have collapsed into a million pieces. Some people say children dying was so common back then that most parents were more surprised if their children lived to be grown than if they passed on. Imagine having babies and expecting them to die. What would be the point? If I'd known Sonny was going to leave me, I'm not sure I would have married him.

Pierce brought us tomatoes right into the fall when Dark Road actually became a little brighter. Dead leaves fell from the trees and covered the ground like a crazy quilt. He slipped over while I was at work and left baskets on the porch, sometimes with a small bunch of marigolds on top.

I tempted Josh with every type of tomato dish I knew how to make. Lasagna, both vegetarian and with meat. Chicken spaghetti. Manicotti with ricotta cheese. Full-bodied tomato soup made by pulverizing cooked tomatoes in the food processor and straining out the seeds. Innumerable lettuce and tomato sandwiches with whole-wheat bread and Hellman's mayonnaise. The tenderest little ravioli patties floating in tomato sauce. Josh perked up, but we were so overloaded with tomatoes that I began giving them to our neighbors who had the same hard red dirt that we did and weren't fortunate enough to have a friend like Pierce.

I looked for Pierce when I passed his house and if he was working outside, I honked and waved. The young boys waved, too, and wanted him to come to dinner again. "One day soon," I answered, knowing full well this wasn't the end of it.

My cooking came to an end when the bank underwent an audit. I drove home after work to pick up the two boys. "Bring along your homework," I said. Josh had to fend for himself. We picked up hamburgers at McDonald's and were back at the bank by 6:00 p.m. The bank examiners came every day that week, going over the ledgers for several months back. I was cooperative, answering questions, furnishing computer printouts, and serving endless cups of coffee. Accounting for money can be very boring for someone like me. I happen to believe it really is easier for a camel to go through the eye of a needle than for a rich man to get to heaven, but then I have no choice. It's fun to be self-righteous when you're poor. However, there is only a certain amount of cooperation I will endure where my family is concerned. At 9:00 sharp I would leave.

My little boys had to go to bed on time.

Two good things came from this. Joshua got out of bed and got dressed. By Friday night, he was sitting at the kitchen table, hammering out rhythms with his hands. "Listen to this," he said. "One, two, THREE, four, one, two THREE, four.

Now listen to this one. One, TWO, one, TWO, one, TWO. Hear the difference?"

"I sure do," I said, allowing myself to give him a little kiss on the top of his head. The birds were singing in his world again.

The second thing was the cream puffs. An old recipe had come into my head during those boring audits. I mixed up the dough, dolloped it on a cookie sheet, and left it in the oven just long enough to form a delicate brown crust. Slicing them like biscuits, I dug out the soft centers. The filling was a custard mixed with whipped cream and laced with sherry the color of an old satin wedding gown. The recipe made several dozen.

Leaving the young boys hammering their hands on the table with Joshua, I put half a dozen cream puffs on my best china plate, the one with the English garden flowers blooming in rose reds and bright yellow. I covered it with a large flowered napkin and drove over to Pierce Landon's house. I'd been alone long enough to get tired of it. After work, I'd scrubbed my skin with Octagon soap until it glowed. My weekday clothes went back in the closet, and I wore a loose Indian cotton dress and two-strap sandals. In the rearview mirror, dust flew out behind my car, a black cloud on a red sunset sky. "Don't lose your nerve now, Lady Tornado," I told myself. "These are the best cream puffs you've ever made."

Pierce's yard was as dark as the graveyard. A sudden wind blew leaves rattling around me. No porch lights. Only one downstairs window glowed dimly. I parked my car and shut the door quietly, making my way across the yard and up the steps with care. At the front door, I froze, my feet glued to the floor. Cool air came up from beneath the porch and my knees began to tremble. I had an urge to run away and go to the cemetery for a talk, but I wasn't sure Sonny would want to hear about this. It seemed like a long time before I could take one hand off the cream puff plate and ring the doorbell, one of those black old-fashioned kind that makes a loud buzz. It gave me a start. His footsteps sounded in the hallway, and he turned on the outside lights so quickly that I was squinting when he opened the door. Those gray-gray eyes with the yellow sparks met mine and all my doubts disappeared into the night.

"Artemis. Come in." Voice low.

I stepped inside and followed Pierce to the living room. The light was on beside a big easy chair where he'd been reading the evening paper. He took the cream puffs and set them on a glass-topped coffee table that let me know a woman had lived in this house at one time. He lifted one up and took a bite, then looked me straight in the eyes. We walked across the hall to a bedroom that smelled musty from disuse. A mahogany framed bed with a faded blue chenille spread took up most of the room. Two soft flowered chairs sat in the shadowy corners like old watchful grandmothers. Pierce opened the windows. A breeze washed over me as soft as his hands and mouth, kissing, nibbling, untying my dress. I kicked my two-strap sandals across the room, and we fell on each other like half-starved children. We tossed and pounded on the long unused bed until a dust cloud formed in the moonlight above us. Pictures of the atomic bomb with its mushroom cloud came into my head. Laughter slid into my heart, pushing the burned edges. It frightened me. The danger of loss still hovered about, popping up to thumb its nose when I least expected it.

"She walked out eight years ago," Pierce explained about his wife. "Just like Martha Gladys, only it was because I stayed home too much. Farming is full time. She did leave the furniture."

"Where did she go?"

"I think she's with a traveling man, maybe someone in the Army. I get post cards. They're always from a different place." We sat up in bed and ate cream puffs and drank wine. "These sure are good," he said. "I'm glad you thought of me, Artemis."

We laughed together. "It's definitely one of my more successful recipes!"

When I got home, the cannibals had cleaned up the rest of the cream puffs and gone to bed.

Saturday morning, I stayed in bed. Turbulence is like a hangover to me. I have to sleep it off. Cartoon noises came from the living room television. Josh was talking to someone on the phone, booking the band for Saturday night. Outside, a truck clattered and complained over the hard dirt road. It got louder as it came down the hill and turned into our driveway. Someone cut the engine. Suddenly, it was quiet except for the music of Herbie Mann and the small beep-beep of a Road-Runner cartoon. I was out of bed in a flash, pulling one of Sonny's old sweatshirts over my nightgown.

Josh and the young boys were already on the front porch.

Pierce got out of his truck. He'd brought along a tractor and two workmen. "Artemis," he said in a good business voice that couldn't hide the way he looked at my bare feet and legs. "We're going to take down a couple of trees right in the center of your yard. Those over there," he said, pointing west. "Girl, you can't grow anything around here if you don't let in some light."

The men were unloading ladders and chainsaws with a chorus of clatter and small talk. My young ones perched on the tractor like monkeys on a gym set. Josh stood there in clean clothes with his hair slicked down, ready to go back to

Birmingham and start playing music again. When he saw what was going on, he went back inside.

At first, my voice wouldn't work. I could feel tears building up. It was nice to think about a vegetable garden and rose bushes for graveyard day, but whoa! This was too sudden for me. It was my property and I made my own decisions. It was time for my Lady Tornado persona to emerge. The bottom line was that I didn't want to be beholden to Pierce, especially if I couldn't pay him back. I looked him in the eyes. "Don't you think we should talk this over?" I said.

Pierce blinked and stepped back, waved his arm at his men to stop. I saw the wariness in his eyes which I'd seen before, but there was a new light, a look of pure stubbornness. "Do you know anything about taking down trees?" he asked.

"No. But, I am the head of this household." I kept my voice steady. "If you want to come inside and discuss prices and payment, I'll give you a cup of coffee." I went through the front screen door quick, swinging it wide, half expecting to hear it bang shut. The boys were still yahooing in the front yard, and Josh was back on the phone again, talking about dates and times. Someone caught the door. The hinges stopped creaking and the floor vibrated with the sound of heavy workboots.

# A Farmer's Wife
## by Dottie McKissac

I would be a farmer's wife and lie down with him at each day's end, day after day, on sun-dried sheets. Lying with his back to me, he would talk about his day in the fields between the rows. He would tell me his tractor woes: the hot sun, his handkerchief beyond wet, wrung-out and hung over the slender rail of the handbrake pull, how he snapped back the wires and cleaned off the heads of the plugs, looking for fire.

I would touch his shoulders and move his muscle slowly with the palm of my hand, caressing away the hurt. "The young corn will be laid-by soon," he would tell me. "I need to grind more shucks and stalks from the crib for the hogs tomorrow. I think the rats have been in there."

Finally, word weary, he turns towards me smiling, "How was your day, Martha?"

"Good," I say and tell him light tales of laundry, sunflowers, Joseph's homework and Ruby's spelling-bee. I leave outside the bedroom door the broken hoe, the rough wringer handle and burned grease.

Slowly the distance between sun-up and sun-down fades. The sheets soften. A welcome breeze moves the curtain. My arm now across his chest, my cheek to his shoulder, my chin rising, our lips touch, "Goodnight, Frank."


Or I could be a dancehall girl.

# Dirt Road

## by Jessica Nelson

When their daddy brought Friday home, the Winthrop kids might as well have won the lottery.

A pickup pulling a rusted trailer followed Vern Winthrop home one day, and a passel of his kids stopped chasing each other around to watch a stranger lead a horse off the trailer. They stood there, red Georgia dirt caking their bare feet, gnats swarming around their heads. Their daddy, a wiry man made of liquor and spite, drank a beer while he watched the other man work. He didn't seem to swallow—he just opened his mouth and let the beer slide down.

"Look at that piece of leather. You ought to pay me to take that nag off your hands!" Vern laughed until his beer threatened to spill. "You gonna take all day or is the horse just that damn slow?"

The man wrenched up his mouth and spat into the dust. Without a word he shoved the lead into some kid's grimy hand, then returned to the pickup to toss a few equine accouterments on top of the dark wet splatter of spittle. Vern threw his now empty can at the back of the trailer as it pulled away.

Five or six children watched him, their frames vibrating with the tension of hope restrained.

"Well, what do you think of that—I done bought you a horse. Now y'all can quit whining all the time about how you want one," Vern announced after a beery belch.

"Really, Daddy, he's ours for real?" At the age of thirteen, Darren was the eldest present. So he took the responsibility of confirming their good fortune.

"Naw, he's mine; but if you're real nice to me I'll let you take care of him. Somebody go grab my cigarettes out of the car." Jimmy, eleven years old and eager to please, took off in a sprint.

"What's his name, Daddy?"

"Hell, I don't know. It's Friday today, so call him that." It was Saturday, but the name stuck.

Martha, age ten and born somewhere in the middle of the eleven total Winthrop children, decided in later years that he probably won the horse in a card game—if for no other reason than it was the first and last time he bought them something they wanted.

All the kids in town rode horses. The Winthrops had always been left out of the plantation rides, as the local kids called it when they gathered in herds and roamed the fields, pastures, and dirt roads on horseback. They would even promenade down the main drag on Sunday afternoons since nothing much else was generally stirring. Talking about horseflesh made them feel grown-up, and they would debate the merits of various breeds while sipping Coca-Cola in the shade. A large family that used to live down by the garbage dump already had enough reasons to feel like outsiders, and the lack of a horse was always sorely felt.

But now the Winthrops had Friday, and they loved him. He was old, swaybacked, and mean; he was contrary, knock-kneed, and did mostly whatever he pleased, but they loved him. The Winthrop kids looked at Friday and saw a marvelous steed. They worked out a riding schedule that was so rigorously fair that everyone was equally dissatisfied with it, and constantly fought over who Friday liked best.

"I gave Friday a crab apple this morning and he didn't even try to bite me," Martha would boast.

"So what, he let me scratch his ears for like ten minutes yesterday," her younger brother Charlie would counter.

Three-year-old Debbie might then yell, "I GAVE FRIDAY A CARROT AND HE SAID HE LIKES CARROTS SO I'M GONNA GIVE HIM ALL MY CARROTS."

They all had their share of nips and near misses from his hooves but they reasoned that if he really meant it, he'd aim better.

The snickers, titters, and guffaws that tended to bubble up in Friday's wake were nothing to the Winthrops. A horse is a horse, as the song goes, and they were far too infatuated with their surly pet to care. And they had plenty of experience ignoring the snubs of others.

On the day that lived in infamy for the rest of the summer, Martha led Friday down the road by the dairy farm for a ride with her best friend, Debra Jones. She noticed Billy Hadley at the end of the road, and stiffened her back in anticipation. Billy was the kind of fifteen-year-old who hung around groups of younger kids so he could push them around. He had blond wiry hair and feet that had reached an adult size before the rest of him, giving him a goonish appearance. This impression was not generally improved on closer acquaintance. A successful feed business made his family wealthy by local standards, which added a sense of entitlement to his inclination for malice.

For some reason Billy saved his worst for Martha—because she was known to be sensitive, or because she read a lot, or maybe because she could throw a football better than he could. But from the beginning he had been one of the most relentless of Friday's persecutors—probably because it was as easy as it was satisfying.

Billy was walking to his grandma's house and stopped for a quick taunt. "Hey, Olive Oyl," he called, "I don't know who has skinnier legs, you or your horse. A good wind'll blow both of you away!"

Martha stopped in front of Debra, who was waiting on her gray dapple mare that had a ferocious carrot habit. They were meeting for a solo ride, as they thought of it when it was only the two of them following dirt roads and talking the mysterious talk of preteen girls.

Debra was fuming even more than Martha was. "I wisht I was as big as Alice Bone," she said. "He wouldn't mess with you no matter how much money he had."

"Don't even look at him," Martha said. "He's all talk, and I don't mind talk. I promise you my daddy talks worse than that."

They walked their horses past Billy with the most dignity two barefoot children in hand-me-down dresses could muster. It was more than enough dignity to further inflame the ugly temper of a boy used to getting his way.

The week before, Billy had decreed that Friday-riding Winthrops were not allowed within two horses of him on rides; this generally meant Billy in front and a nose full of dust for Friday's rider. Emboldened, perhaps, by the fact that it was Martha and not an older brother, the older boy seemed to decide the time was ripe for escalation.

If Darren hadn't been walking by, the heavy, sharp-edged piece of quartz Billy launched would certainly have hit Martha. She heard a loud "Hey!" and jerked around to see Billy's missile fly past her face into the bushes. "What are you doing, creep?" Darren yelled at Billy.

Billy squared off and said, "Using your horse for target practice. Somebody needs to put him out of his misery, anyway."

Smelling a fight in the air, some Winthrops and a few other kids appeared in a loose circle around the two boys. Billy was older, bigger, and meaner, but Darren was a bigger smart ass. Any way you cut it, it was a win for spectators.

"What's your problem, Hadley? Are you flirting with my sister or is it the horse you're in love with?"

"Ooooooo," goaded the watchers.

"You're the one in love with your own stupid horse," Billy the wit said.

"He's better looking than you are anyway," Darren fired back. Fists clenched, head lowered, worn-out tennis shoes planted in the clay, Darren was losing his sense of humor.

"Oh, yeah?" Billy said, searching for a comeback.

"And you know what else?" Darren continued, losing his head altogether. "Our horse is worth you and that pony you ride put together."

"In your dreams, you little twerp. I can run faster myself than your horse on my own two feet."

Darren always did have more sass than he had sense, and he challenged Billy Hadley to a horse race right there.

Billy bent over, holding his stomach in an exaggerated pose of hilarity. He stayed like that for a long time giving big fake guffaws for effect. "Any time, kid. Sounds like you need to be put in your place anyway." Though he agreed to it, he only half expected Darren to follow through.

"Fine. After lunch, right here on this road. If you ain't shamed to get beat by Friday."

They were still standing in the middle of the baked clay road lined with wild plum trees that eventually passed by the ramshackle Winthrop homestead. The sun and gnats had risen, and drops of sweat collected on Billy Hadley's top lip, which was also home to a nearly invisible fringe of pale mustache.

"So what do I get when I win?"

"What?" asked Darren, who had not thought that far ahead.

"What do I get for winning? Make it worth my time. I'll stop making fun of Friday if you win, so what do I get if I win?"

"We won't go on rides with you anymore?"

"For starters. Plus y'all have to admit any time I ask that your horse is a worthless piece of crap."

Watching from horseback, Martha felt her stomach do that sickly lurch that it did when she saw someone get hurt, or when she walked up on her father suddenly in an otherwise empty room. Avoiding Billy wouldn't be a hardship, but betraying Friday—high stakes indeed.

Darren was still mad but looked a little anxious as he said "Deal," shook Billy's hand, and then walked away. Martha waited with Debra for the other kids to disperse, then got down and walked Friday back to their house for the war council. The horse was impatient, and dragged her along so fast she nearly lost her feet.

There were four Winthrop kids who were old enough or young enough to be concerned in the matter: Darren, Jimmy, Martha, and Charlie, in order of birth. They squatted in a huddle in the front yard as Debbie and Carl, two of the younger ones, crowded against their backs trying to find out what was going on.

The four looked at each other and looked at their chances.

"Who gets to ride?" Jimmy asked.

"I can ride," Charlie said. "Friday likes me best anyway."

"Does not!" Martha interrupted. She had an empathetic nature, and was certain she and Friday shared a most precious and secret bond of friendship. "I was supposed to ride him today anyway, so it should be me."

"You don't know how to ride for real," Charlie said. "Girls can't race, everybody knows."

Darren forestalled their philosophical argument on the abilities of girls. "Jimmy is the smallest, so he should be the jockey," he said.

They all fell silent and looked at Jimmy. Jimmy had it rough. He was small and wiry in a family of tall reedy kids, and he was a bed wetter. Big families often have one kid who is the butt of all the jokes, and the Winthrops had Jimmy for that. Their mama and daddy were the most merciless; whether it was because he was a bed wetter or whether he was a bed wetter because his mama and daddy picked on him, no one cared to ask. Mostly the other kids were just glad when it was someone else getting picked on.

Now they all looked at scrawny Jimmy with skepticism and speculation. He turned blotchy red around the neck. "I can do it. Lemme ride him."

The other three exchanged looks and Martha traced some curlicues in the dirt. The family honor wasn't much, but they were reluctant to trust it to the least of them. Then with more confidence than she felt, Martha said on impulse, "I vote for Jimmy." Just like that it was settled. None of them spoke much as they gobbled some leftover biscuits and jelly for lunch, and then Darren sent Jimmy to walk Friday around some neighboring pasture.

As race-time approached, kids began gathering along the road. Billy brought his glossy quarter horse out and got him to prance in front of the line someone had gouged in the road. Martha and Charlie fidgeted until finally Jimmy and Friday ambled over from off to the side. Following Darren's instructions, Jimmy kept Friday turned away from the starting line. The horse turned an irritated eye on the crowd and stood working his mouth. They noticed for the first time that he did look shabby next to the Hadley horse and then regretted thinking it.

Anticipation was running high, even among those least concerned. In a sleepy town where you usually had to make your own excitement, a horse race was Big News, even if the conclusion was foregone. A few kids tried to wager baseball cards or candy on the outcome, but no one wanted to bet on Friday.

Martha had watched Jimmy and Friday walk up to the starting line with her stomach in her throat. Her stomach did that little jump again when she looked at Jimmy perched on top of the beat-up saddle. He looked so delicate with his elbows sticking out like bony wings. The chuckles around her were suddenly unbearable.

A few kids were dispatched to the end of the half-mile track to serve as judges, and Jimmy let Friday turn toward the starting line. He seemed to be having some trouble keeping control and was pulling on the reins. Debra Jones stood off to the side and yelled "Ready!" Jimmy hunched down even smaller. "Set!" Billy Hadley sneered at no one in particular. "Go!"

They were off, and Martha took off after them. Her bare feet slapped against the dirt road and her heart pounded in her ears, drowning out the yells around her for a moment. She ran with elbows and knees flying, praying for a miracle. Dust obscured the racers as Martha silently chanted to the beat of her foot falls. "Go, Jimmy, go. Go, Jimmy, go."

What no one but the Winthrops saw coming was Friday's affinity for home. He liked the place where little loving hands were always ready to caress him or smuggle him apples. Darren had set up the race so that Friday was pointed towards the house with its little patch of grass that Friday knew was his. At one time or another almost every one of the Winthrops had been on Friday's back when he realized he was headed toward home. He ran for home like wolves were nipping at his heels. That day, in fact, Martha's legs and arms still bore the thin scabbed-over cuts from the previous week when Friday took off for home through Alice Bone's loose hedge of thorny shrubs.

It was over quickly. When Martha reached the end of the road, panting and sweaty, Darren and a few allies were hoisting Jimmy over their heads. Martha's hoarse victory yell went unheard in the clamor, and her glasses fogged up a little. Friday strolled over to his picket to start munching grass. Jimmy looked as wildly happy as she'd ever seen him, grinning from ear to ear and holding on to Darren's shoulder. No one could believe the outcome, and both horse and boy were wreathed in a fleeting glory. Martha ran to her brothers, jumping and whooping, and forgot every indignity of her life. For the moment, the least were first and she was joyful.

# Heifers

## by Judith Nunn

When the late afternoon sun lit the white faces of the Herefords turned toward the farmhouse, Elizabeth thought they were beautiful. Their large, fringed eyes were fully trusting. She liked the way their short hair curled in different directions, like that on a Chihuahua-mix dog she had when she was eight. And that was all she knew about cows the fourth month after she married Bob Bingham.

Bob got rid of cows that bucked or bellowed, looked at him wrong, or showed any kind of spirit. He was raising Herefords because he found them docile. But he also knew young Herefords sometimes had narrow hipbones, so he was careful to buy bulls that promised small calves.

One late July afternoon he came home, his shirt lying flat and wet against his chest. A neighbor's bull had gotten into his pasture through a break in the east fence and he by God knew it and could count the months back, because his favorite heifer was now straining to deliver a calf. He called the vet's office, but the receptionist said it could be hours before he was out of surgery, so Bob stomped back out to the truck to do what he could. He was late coming in to supper.

"The front feet were out," he said, "but I couldn't pull the calf. Damn it, she was lying in briars, up against a sweetgum, and when I braced myself I could sometimes see the white face, but I couldn't get the shoulders through."

Elizabeth had cooked a roast with potatoes and a side of rattlesnake beans, knowing there was trouble on their farm. His farm. It belonged halfway still to his father, and she reckoned the cows were half his, too. She had set the table with flowered plates, a wedding present she found ordinary, and Betty Crocker silver, because he didn't like what he called "putting on airs," especially when things weren't going well.

She liked fixing up the old farmhouse with her grandmother's French antiques. More than anything she wanted to give him a baby. She didn't even have second thoughts about a baby when he talked of that heifer and calf dying.

It did seem, though, that discussions about cows were always about reproduction. Male calves had to be cut, neutered. True, they also needed vaccinating with the inoculants he kept in the refrigerator next to the mayonnaise. And worming. Posts were strung with hanging burlap soaked in something foul to discourage the flies they swatted with their tails. But the main interest seemed to be in making the males sterile and then selling them in the spring after they'd grown on grass and hay over the winter. There could be only one bull in the pasture.

It was the heifers she felt real sympathy for. She had heard talk of heifer pastures, but they didn't have one yet. The heifers ranged with the herd. That's what made it so critical that the bull have small calves, because the heifers came into heat (she didn't know any other word for it) at various times, and could be bred before they were large enough to birth calves. Well, Bob did separate six bought heifers once, put them down at the FHA pasture, but they got into something and she was in the truck when he found them staggering and shivering, some on the ground unable to get up. He took one of them to the university but they all died and she never heard why.

"You've got to have another job to be able to afford cows," he grumbled. He didn't like black cows. He had bought a black heifer with a white face once, but she had gotten in the road, and Truit Smith had run his truck into the ditch to miss her. Then she caught herself in barbed wire, way over behind the pond near the back pines, and had torn the fence down struggling, letting the neighbor's cows in again. It had taken two days to separate the herds. Elizabeth had cooked meat loaf, mashed potatoes, and field peas that week.

Bob just didn't like black cows. Angus was the breed gaining popularity in the South, but he didn't trust them. He stuck with his red Herefords. There was even talk of more exotic breeds at the county fair, like Keoninas, but he would have none of it.

At her medical checkup before the wedding, the doctor had pointed out that since Bob was older, she might want to start a family soon. They had married in the late fall after the soybeans and cotton were in. Bob disappeared into the woods in the afternoons to hunt quail and later deer and then, in the early spring, turkey. She was making draperies to cut down on drafts. The house that had been his grandfather's was cold, so cold that first winter that her favorite vase froze and broke sitting on the dining table they had made from a door. One morning they woke to see a tiny mouse sitting by the fireplace, the only source of heat in their bedroom, though the logs were by then only ash and a few coals.

She wasn't pregnant. Mother's Day came early with a promise of softening in the air which was warm enough for open windows in the frame church. Her voice cracked on the second phrase of "How Precious Is a Mother's Love..." and she turned from the hymnal to watch a small fly crawl across the pew in front.

The service was going to last past noon, and her roast would be overdone. While the preacher praised the self-sacrificing mother she longed to be, she began to listen to the traffic on the state highway outside, trying to hold back tears.

That afternoon she walked with Bob down to the pond he had built the fall before. The grass was beginning to green, and the breeze bent the broom sage as they followed the cow trail through the pasture. Elizabeth was wondering how cows so wide could make only a ten-inch path when Bob said, "That cow is barren." He was pointing with his index finger at a fat, rather young heifer.

He didn't say any more until they passed the shade of the oaks and sweet gums where most of the herd had gathered. "That one is barren, too," he added, indicating the patient face staring back at him. "I'm going to sell those two."

While Bob walked across the dam to check the back fence, she waited, lying prostrate on the narrow dock of the pond. Her forehead on her hands, she grieved for the heifers. She grieved for all things barren. When she had cried herself empty, she propped on her elbows and looked out over the pond. She was thinking the dock was just wide enough for a small child to sit on the end and splash his feet.

# Soft Focus

by Judith Nunn

Each spring and summer I carry a picture of you
Standing between the tomatoes and the butterbeans
Holding a hoe, looking up, unsmiling, as if interrupted
From your early-morning focus.

I walk through wet grass to see you,
Standing on the old barn site, the amended soil,
Wearing jeans worn soft and thin by work,
A denim shirt bleached sheer by sun and salt.

If your disciplined feet didn't move,
The soles of your boots would grow roots.
You've been there for years, hoeing weeds
In the rows you said I didn't tend.

I bought asparagus crowns, on sale,
And proudly planted them in space you gave me.
But sure they wouldn't grow, you bought your own
And set them, slightly raised, in the row above.

For many springs we steamed the stems,
Yours green, mine white,
Until you brought manure from the pasture,
And grubs which ate the roots of all, equally.

You planted green peppers; I planted yellow.
You planted cantaloupe; I planted larkspur.
Your eggplants were large and fat, mine long and slim.
And you hoed my rows as well.

Now I reach to pull weeds from a small raised bed
Of bought and composted soil over earth of clay and rock.
This morning, as I dug new very-blue potatoes, I saw you,
Still standing in the old rows, but you had the hint of a smile.

# I Can't
## by Charlene Redick

Victoria Love Brace was a beautiful woman with that aggregate of qualities that gives pleasure to the senses and exalts the spirit, and she was particularly graceful and ornamental in a crowd. She was also of excellent quality of mind and she went to lengths, often exceeding the ordinary, to grasp a situation or give relief.

She had been told that she was beautiful many times by men—on airplanes, including an Air Canada French flight steward who brought her a glass of champagne and stood at her seat and said, "You are very beautiful"; by an African-American gentleman who was shopping at Kroger on his lunch hour just as she was, and who walked by her and murmured, "Mmmm, mmm, mmmm!"; by two little boys who were friends of her son who took hold of her hair in the park one day, as she sat on a blanket reading, and spread it out like wings and danced with her hair; by four male students who sat at the base of the U of the inter-joined tables in her history class and took bets on which one would bed her; and by her doctor who gave her to his female partner. Over and over these compliments came to her, and so she developed several ways to deflect them because they often meant "I want to fuck you."

Her best friend Claire said to her, "You don't see how their eyes follow you when you come in a room and when you leave. It's a hormone stampede."

She ignored Claire. Men flirted around to get back at their wives who carried their balls in their purses, or because they were afraid of losing it sexually, which often led them to losing it in the area of decorum. Claire carried a gun, and said that Victoria should do so, too, and lift it high into view when a guy asked for a piece.

For the most part, Victoria was tender about men's attraction to her because, usually, sexual vulgarity was not what they dumped at her feet: gross, insulting, overt come-ons: "Hey, baby, sit on my face. Fucky, sucky, fucky, sucky."

What she got, instead, was a kind of muted, plaintive howl of hunger for female acknowledgement petitioned from her—a source that obviously represented the element of feminine totality in a woman that they discerned could be trusted, based in large part, she knew, on a quality that went beyond her female pulchritude: her sympathetic nature.

They were therefore willing to stand before her, in their lust afflictions, and request the rules of engagement for the sacrificial ordeal that lay ahead: the slinging themselves over a cliff for a woman. She had deep empathy for them. To be doomed to such active peril in the heedless pursuit of acquiring the affection and sexual favors of a woman was lyrical and often so tragic that it was mythical in its proportions.

Still, it made many things uncomfortable: her relationships with other women, for instance, especially if they had a man and were afraid of losing him; dressing so that her cleavage was covered so as not to encourage sexual come-ons; hostile stares from perfect strangers, usually women, again; gossip that she was ungodly; resentment of her presence at mixed gatherings; distrust of her motives; being excluded from parties simply from a threat-management aspect; envy of her influence; but mostly women deliberately eschewing any involvement with her based on their decision that she was too dangerous to include.

She knew this was all related to the fact that men were visual animals and inordinately susceptible to mental images attained or maintained by sight, but what could she do about it? She didn't want anybody else's boyfriend or husband. Her sweet nature was not a siren song.

Would this situation resolve itself if she stayed in her house? Or cut off her hair and permed it into a Brillo pad? Or stopped wearing the make-up that made her blue eyes pop? Or let her grooming go? Or changed her scent from evocative French floral to a camphor-based talcum powder?

She wasn't going to become a recluse or grow herself ugly or mean just to fit in. So what if she caused a riot in Walmart or if men looked at her as if she were the sun rising in the east when she came into the room, or turned away abashed? What was the point of making herself hideous just so the rest of the world would stay calm? Hope was important, and in some ancient, secret way she knew she gave out hope.

So she usually ignored the male come-on—or acknowledged it when the nod or smile felt like a compliment and let men carry on, kindly refusing their drinks and other offers, taking no notice of their overt whistles and stares, and turning away from their eyes undressing her—the eye-ball raping, Claire called it and got on with her work. There were worse problems than being a bombshell, even if the country was at war.

Which was why it was easy enough to see how it all began: in the Auburn City Library—a small need, a look across the room, eye contact, an encounter, and then a conversation heavy with portents. But staggeringly incomprehensible how it ended: as a riddle, an ending that gave nothing. No answers, no quarter, no mercy, no relief, the definite bringing to a stop, the destroyed outcome, the cessation of hope; the non-reaching of a specified and ultimate rank or situation, the close of possibility, the "death of" what might have been.

Sad and regrettable and all the adjectives and phrases that describe the loss of a cherished desire, of anticipation, of expectation of obtainment: gone in sixty seconds, a gross misunderstanding never made right, the missed opportunity, the road not taken, the known world altered, the nadir, the abyss, the chance that comes no more.

It began in the reading room, where she was a regular, going in every other morning and sitting at the last station on the last row, and staying for about an hour reading newspapers and magazines. He usually came in after her, and was one row up. He got up often—the bathroom, to get a smoke—she didn't know, but he was a restless person, and it distracted her. Perhaps he had spinal problems and couldn't sit for long. Maybe he had arthritis of the knee.

He was a fascinating physical specimen—fair, bald, in terrific shape, and about sixty years old, with compelling blue eyes and a thoughtful countenance. When she saw him looking so gracefully around the open bay reading room at all the patrons, including her, and then standing pensively and studying -- through the huge floor to ceiling windows—the red and orange of the crepe myrtle trees outside, the song that Frank Sinatra sang about beautiful girls walking a little slower and children shooting at bad men hit her right above the heart.

This isn't cool, she thought. He looks like a benevolent Vladimir Putin but I don't need a cold war, or to get off track, and I don't want all the accommodation that comes with letting a man into my life: the knocks on the door late when you both know what he wants; the moving into the anticipatory mode in everyday life with its attendant anxiety as you take his preferences and wishes into account; the self-criticism that inevitably follows every exchange; and your obsession with everything about yourself—your looks, scent, hygiene, politics, preferences, and past—and whether it measures up. Nope, don't need this. I've got major work to do. Stop this now. Turn away. No. No. And again, No!

Her thesis was on the moral imagination of the artist and how it is compromised —a topic she was excited about. She wasn't sure what she was going to do with a graduate degree in Modern Literature—especially in this day and age—but she was back in college getting more education, which she had delayed while raising her children, and enjoying all the novels she was reading in her studies. When her husband died, she was left with a two-hundred thousand dollar life insurance policy and a small cottage on Payne Street in Auburn that she had moved into after selling their big house, which was on Samford and worth a great deal, as everybody was buying property for retirement and the football game weekends.

Harrison, her husband, had worked for the Associated Press and taught journalism at Auburn University. They had lived here quietly all their married life. Their children were now educated and established: an elementary school teacher, banker, caterer and events planner, and an engineer. She didn't know why they were not drawn to the arts with a mother who was in literature and a father who was a journalist, but that was that.

She had always kept a low profile in the town and this did not change with widowhood, putting the four hundred thousand dollars from the house into investments and living off the interest from the insurance proceeds, and occasionally traveling. She had never been this well off in her life. They had always struggled, with mortgages on everything, and cars that were years old and the educational needs of four children. None of that mattered now. The children were grown, all four of them, and Harrison was gone—a year now. He died in six weeks from a cancer that had almost killed her as well. For better or worse, she had lived her marriage and faced the death of her spouse—an agonizing endurance test.

Now she was totally free, and so this management of her beauty and the possibilities that came with it, which her love for Harrison had always sheltered her from, fell totally on her shoulders, which meant that for safety's sake she had continued wearing her wedding rings and stayed in a lot.

It didn't take long to discover that he was a Russian and a Jew. He stopped at her cubicle asking if she had a pencil sharpener in her pen case, which she did. He borrowed it and brought it back. He was tall like Phillip Roth, pale like Joseph Heller, wrinkled in all the humor places like Kurt Vonnegut, and discerning of physical beauty like Saul Bellow. If he had hair he would have looked like Jeff Bridges. But he didn't have hair, so when he brought the sharpener back, she looked closely and saw that it looked as if he shaved his hair off, rather than its falling out from the effects of chemo poisons. And so she asked, "Do you shave your head?"

"Yes," he replied.

His voice was deep and held evidence of his origins—an American accent, Great Lakes region, with a slight burr and flat vowels. She immediately thought of

Bellow's challenge that writers be beacons for civilization and awaken the world from intellectual torpor.

"Why do you shave your head?"

"You don't like it?"

His response flustered her and her question, she thought, must have given him pause, but given the recent loss of her spouse to leukemia, baldness had resonating portents.

"I beg your pardon." She turned away. Such an intimate exchange right here at the beginning—what was she thinking?

"I shave it to save time. I travel all over the world."

She felt in him an immense, painful longing for a fuller, more coherent and comprehensive account of what we human beings are, who we are and what this life is, and as he stood there at the cubicle wanting her attention, it shook her.

"I see." She turned away again.

"Ask me another question. I'll answer it. We're not bothering anybody. People have lost their lives in libraries. They ought to be warned."

This comment was so close to a Bellow quote that she thought the man before her might actually be Saul Bellow, but then she remembered that Bellow had died on April 5, 2005, at age eighty-nine, and was buried at the Jewish cemetery in Brattleboro, Vermont.

She thought he might stutter through the standard explanations that are the response to most of life's questions—I outgrew it; I couldn't manage it, or my direction changed—so she decided that she would ask the four questions that she depended on that allowed her to gauge where a man stood and what he wanted.

"Do you and your wife have children?"

"Indeed, and grandchildren, although my wife is no longer with me. She died of radiation sickness after the Chernobyl accident."

Victoria was shocked. "I'm so sorry!"

"Thank you. Four hundred times more fallout was released than in the atomic bombing of Hiroshima. 1986. I was thirty-nine years old. It launched my career as an international consultant."

"I see. Are you radioactive?"

"No. I was not there when the accident occurred. I was in Berlin. "

Then she asked her second question: "How did you get here?"

"I live in Peachtree City, Georgia, close to the Atlanta airport, which I use frequently, but I'm in Auburn every week."

This made sense, especially if he were on the faculty.

"What kind of work do you do?"

"I consult in nuclear engineering at the university. For some reason, suddenly, the quote comes to mind: *A great deal of intelligence can be invested in ignorance when the need for illusion is deep.*

And the fourth question, if she didn't know by now, was always, "Do you have a lady?" But he had answered that question already. "Thank you for the use of the pencil sharpener."

"Sure."

"I would like to take you . . . for coffee. Would you like a coffee, when you are done with your work?" His words were high lyricism as though he were in love with the luxurious pleasure of language itself.

Take you . . . Whoa!

She froze. Was she going to let this happen? Did she even want to start this up for any reason other than he was physically and culturally interesting? What could be gained from knowing a man intimately who was from the world of nuclear accidents and Polonium poison swirling in cups of English tea? Was she even up to the effort and energy required to open her life to the strife and accommodation that came with letting a man—one that may be a KGB agent—in?

She shook her head. "I can't."

"We should go to the Amsterdam Café over on Gay Street, and sit outside on this lovely September morning, and you can tell me the story of your life."

She shook her head firmly. "I have too much work to do."

"I want to talk to you. I come here every morning just to look at you. You are what would be called, in my home country, an American classic."

"What do you mean?"

"A young widow, still in your forties, yes? Anglican origins—British, right? Beautiful in the classic sense—proportioned, gorgeous face with beautiful facial planes, abundant hair? Studying Saul Bellow, who can never sit still when it comes to women, can never keep his zipper zipped."

She shook her head and smiled at his forthrightness.

"His womanizing doesn't come from strength. He's afraid of dying."

"You mean his characters, of course?'

"He, as well. He was married five times. And he moved from leftist politics to neo-conservatism, and fought with feminists, campus revolutionaries, and postmodernists, and thrust himself into the often contentious realm of Jewish and African-American relations. But who knows really? I go with the theory that the writer is always working something out with his characters."

"Saul would have fallen for you. He loves women who are the feminine embodiment."

"Did you know Saul Bellow?"

"We were neighbors in Vermont, my summer home. Both from Chicago." He looked at the stack of her mail on the library table next to Bellow's book, *More Die of Heartbreak*. "I see you have the Victoria Secret catalog." She was mortified. She had picked up the mail from the post office earlier and the catalog was stuck in between the power bill and her BankAmerica statement. He picked up the catalog. "What's your secret, Victoria?" He murmured as he turned the pages. This is an omen, she thought, as her heart flipped. He looked deep into her eyes as he turned the pages. "What's your name?"

"Victoria."

"You're kidding?"

"No." She smiled and shook her head. "No."

They laughed.

He gave her back the catalogue. "I'll ask you again another time."

She nodded with relief. "Thank you."

He went back to his work. She went back to her work. After a few minutes, she left quietly and went to her class on the 20th-Century Jewish Novelist.

She didn't go back to the library for several days, and when she did, there was no trace of Vladimir, as she called him. His cubicle was occupied by a knurled old geezer who turned the pages of the week's newspapers looking for the Georgia lottery picks, and announced all the news to the patrons sitting around him: "Palin shoots moose from a plane." "Paul Newman's got lung cancer." "Hurricane Ike's comin."

Nor was he there the following three times she went, nor any other time she visited the library to study, as it was quieter than the university library, and had all of Saul Bellow.

# Mr. Hardcastle
## by Charlie Rose

After Katie and I called it quits, she took up with this ball bearing salesman, Freddie Snipes, and they got married and moved to Valdosta, Georgia. Freddie Snipes wanted to adopt my son Tommy, but I wasn't letting him do that, even though the child support was hurting me. In the last four months, I had only been to visit Tommy once, and that hadn't turned out well. I got into it with Freddie Snipes, over being behind on the child support. Katie had to pull me off of him.

Lately, I had been spending my Sunday afternoons fishing on the Alabama River with Cole Hoskins. He was a house painter at Dixie Paint. His trailer was down the road from mine, and if you kept on going down that road you got to the Alabama River. I still went fishing with Cole Sunday afternoons even though Cole's wife Charlene and I were seeing each other on Saturday afternoons. Cole made it easy for me to be with Charlene. On Saturday afternoon he took their daughter, Dyan, their little four year old, downtown with him; she was with him shaking a tambourine while he preached on a street corner half a block from the state liquor store.

One Sunday afternoon while we were fishing, Cole told me about his eye problem. He had trouble reading his Bible unless he kept his left eye closed. They came and went, these zigzagging motes in his eyes. He was afraid he might be going blind, and he didn't know what to do about it.

I was still doing odd jobs for my neighbor across the road, Elinor Williams. I'd replaced I don't know how many thirty-amp fuses for Elinor. Elinor used to tell me the next time she married it wouldn't be for love or money. She'd marry a man who knew how to do the things she couldn't do for herself. After I put in a float in Elinor's toilet tank one Saturday afternoon, I brought up Cole's vision problem. Elinor looked up at me from a novel she was reading, sipped on her Canadian Mist and soda. I felt the sun's flat rays heat up my neck and moved my lawn chair in toward Elinor.

"Cole says he won't go to an eye doctor."

I knew Elinor would set me straight. "Who says he has to, Wesley?" All my friends but her call me Wes. I'm just beginning to get used to Wesley from her. "Tell Cole he should go to a drugstore and buy a pair of readers. That would be a lot cheaper than going to an eye doctor." She took another big sip on her Canadian. I didn't know how she put so much away every day. Catch her early enough in the afternoon, what she said still made some kind of sense. "All Cole has to do is put his readers on and he can read his Bible to his heart's content. You tell Cole these drugstore glasses are cheap. He can get a pair for nine ninety-five. I'm sure that's what you must want to tell him so I won't say anymore about it now."

Elinor dipped down to her book, waiting for me to say something. Instead I asked myself just what had made her settle down in this trailer park. She liked it here by the river, with your kind of people, she told me once, because she was so far away from the people she'd known while she'd been married to Rutherford. She'd moved back here from Athens, Georgia, to not far from where she'd grown up, which was just this side of Wetumpka. Rutherford was a paleontologist at the University of Georgia. She had never had much in common with him, so their marriage hadn't lasted very long. Rutherford would talk your ear off about fossils, she'd say, but he didn't know beans about the human heart. She'd say the human heart, for Rutherford, was just a muscle.

The novels Elinor read meant nothing to Rutherford, less than nothing he used to tell her, because they weren't about people who did something in the real world. I didn't know Rutherford, didn't want to. But he might have been right about Elinor's novels. She kept them in her mother's bookcase, a golden oak job with glass doors which she had with her now, in her trailer. The binding was loose on the novel she was reading—a long one with pen and ink illustrations, a Victorian novel, she'd told me once. I offered to slap some tape on it, but she knew I had this other thing on my mind. She was waiting for me to get to Charlene Hoskins.

Instead I asked her about Mr. Hardcastle, what was he up to today, in what looked like about two fingers worth of her novel. "Is Mr. Hardcastle still blaming the wind for how he feels?" I asked her, swinging my foot up across my knee. Mr. Hardcastle blamed everything on the wind. If the wind was blowing from the north, he'd say that's why I'm pissed off today. From the south, hey man I feel just great. From the east he'd be crying a bucket. From the west he didn't give a shit about anybody. "I never knew a dude like Mr. Hardcastle," I told her.

"Well you see he's a little eccentric. That's how he's supposed to be. The wind can do Mr. Hardcastle that way because he's a character in a novel."

"You ask me, he's a weirdo."

"You, Wesley, might think so because you don't know what winds blow your life around."

"Are you telling me I'm not in control of my life?"

"I'm only saying you could be more in control. So for that matter could Mr. Hardcastle. That's why he's in this book, so the reader can judge for himself how wrong it is for Mr. Hardcastle to attribute everything he feels to the direction of the wind. His putting everything on the wind is irresponsible of him. If you read this book you would see that."

I sensed Elinor was floating up over the pines, above the trailers, way up over the river, and since I didn't want to pop her little balloon I said, "If you ever get finished with that novel, you lend it to me and I'll read it. I mean carefully."

"Yes, carefully, Wesley. That you should do."

I let the subject of Mr. Hardcastle alone because I had something else to talk to Elinor about. I told Elinor Charlene and I had had a fight last Saturday, last time I'd seen her. Instead of dragging her off downtown so she could shake that tambourine, Cole had taken Dyan to see Charlene's grandparents in Montgomery. I had to tell Charlene she should be the one to do that. That should be your job, not Cole's, I told her. Charlene told me to stay out of her life with Cole. I said I'd try to do that in the future, and she said we wouldn't have a future if I didn't give her and Cole some respect.

I got a strong beam of disapproval, not Elinor's usual fuzzy focusing. "Here you are sleeping with this woman and you think you should run her life. If Charlene stopped washing the dishes for Cole, you'd probably come down on her for that." Reaching over to pick up her glass, she let her other hand run through her matted gray hair like she needed to loosen it up. "Let me tell you something, Wesley. I tried sleeping around for awhile. About a year after Rutherford left me I would go to the bar at the Holiday Inn. I'd go on week nights, when men my age were there. They'd be moving on the next day, so both of us knew what the score was. But Charlene, she obviously doesn't know the score. She thinks she can keep Cole for a husband and have you on Saturday afternoons."

"Remind me to ask her what she thinks. I mean who knows what goes on in Charlene's head?"

"You don't know because you don't want to. You're only interested in yourself."

I saw a lizard crawling off the patio and thought of Cole going blind. He wouldn't be able to lace his boots or squint down the barrel of a shotgun. Charlene came out of their trailer and dropped a bag of garbage in the garbage can. She had on the tight cutoffs she was wearing the first time I knocked on her door. She waved at me from down the road, and I waved back, knowing I'd go to her unless Cole and Dyan came back from downtown while I was sitting here. If he did I'd tell him what Elinor told me, you get some readers and see if they don't help you see better.

150

Cole wasn't worried about going blind anymore. He had bought a pair of readers, and right away the zigzagging motes went away, and he was able to read his Bible again. He put them on while we were ordering our lunch at Burger King, reading off today's specials to me. He took them off while he ate his Whopper, wiping his fingers carefully once he'd popped the last fry into his mouth. He picked the readers up and carefully hooked the temples over his ears, just to make sure they were still working.

Cole got to talking about Bible movies, what Hollywood did to the Bible, twisted and changed it, Cole said. I asked Cole why that mattered since some of the things in the Bible plain just didn't happen. I said no one Israelite could slay that many Philistines with the jawbone of an ass. Cole's blue eyes never wavered. "What you don't understand when you say that, Wes, is what the good Lord is showing us. He's showing us He can intervene in our lives just like He did in their lives. He helped Samson smite his enemies, and then He punished Samson for sinning."

"So how would the Lord intervene in your life? What does Samson have to do with you?"

Cole spoke slowly, without raising his voice. "Samson's story has everything to do with me. It warns me to shun the harlot's bed. I'm a man. I can be tempted. I was tempted and I gave in. The Lord has seen fit to punish me."

I didn't want to ask how it happened. I made myself look at Cole's blue eyes, still set on the path he was following.

"Charlene had gone to the Gulf Coast with Dyan to see her mama. I was painting houses at the time. We had this woman in our crew. Rena Latham. Rena asked me to take her home one Friday night."

"That all you have to tell me, Cole?"

"No, that's just the beginning. Saturday morning, Rena Latham shows up at my house. She's all dressed up, ringing the doorbell on me. She's wearing this pretty flowered dress. I was hoping I had locked the door, but I hadn't. I didn't know what to do next."

"So you waited for her to come in. Or you went to the door and let her in?"

"She had walked from her house to my house. I went to the door and let her in."

A man and his wife and two teenage girls wearing shorts and not much on top came in, moved on to gawk at the specials. I heard something beep, the French fry machine, or maybe it was an oven somewhere, letting us know that its time was up, whatever was in the oven. We won't be letting you guys out alive, was what the beeper might have been saying.

"I knew right then I would pay for it, but for a long time nothing happened to me. Then one night in that same house Charlene and I were together in bed. We heard someone ring the doorbell. Charlene said I should answer it and I told her, Charlene it's midnight. I told her someone must have the wrong house, but that doorbell kept on ringing."

"And you answered it?"

"No way," Cole said. "I let the doorbell ring until it stopped."

"Are you saying that had something to do with the Lord?"

"I'm saying it did," Cole said. "I'm saying it was like the Bible says, when the Lord comes down on sinners. He was letting me know I'd done wrong before He came down on me for it."

I had to ask Cole how the Lord came down on him. Cole didn't hesitate to tell me how.

"The next time I tried to make love to Charlene, I couldn't do anything, Wes. It's been going on for a long time now, ever since I heard that doorbell ringing."

Coming back with their trays of fast food, this family had nothing to say to us, not the father with his tiny mustache or the mother with her big handbag swinging and swaying and bumping her hip, the girls with their acne and silly talk, they kept to themselves. Cole put his head in his hands. I looked at Cole's coffee getting cold, the slashed pink packets of sweetener.

I had sex with Charlene again while Cole was preaching downtown. There were the two of them on a street corner, Cole preaching, Dyan shaking the tambourine. I passed them on my way to the state liquor store for tequila and margarita mix. I thought of stopping and listening to Cole. He had a permit to use speakers, so his voice carried all the way to my car. He had to compete with the traffic, a burring monotone of passing vehicles. Cole was going on about Sodom. The Sodomites were hardened sinners. Lot never should have tried to reason with them. Nobody paid Cole any attention, not even when Cole brought in fire and brimstone.

Cole wouldn't be fishing with me for awhile, not on his Sunday afternoons. He would be painting his church, working for the Lord, he told me at Burger King, the French fry machine dinging away. I told him he didn't have to sacrifice his Sunday afternoons, and he said since he'd talked to me he'd decided he had to serve the Lord first.

"Charlene says I should get paid for painting the church, that our church can afford to pay me. I've thought about that a lot, how much it means to me now not to get paid." Cole's simple blue eyes bored into mine. "I mean it's helping me accept the Lord's will," he said. "That's all that matters."

"For you. But what about Charlene? What about your little girl Dyan? Don't they matter?" I wanted to get across to him he'd better climb down off that church steeple.

"Of course they matter. Don't you understand, Wes, if I'm right with the Lord, then I'll be right with them too."

So I did my fishing by myself, and for awhile I felt that was the right thing to do. Cole would go his own way, and I would go mine. A crosswind was blowing my line around, so I had to shift my boat around so the stern was into the wind. I got to thinking about Mr. Hardcastle, would the wind have affected his fishing? What would it be like to be him, I thought. If the wind was right would I be a good man and give up this thing with Charlene? Would a north wind make me blow my top and a south wind cause me to laugh like hell or like Mr. Hardcastle ride my good steed over the moors, and let no one get in my way? Would a west wind send me back to my bed with the drapes pulled and the lights out?

It was time to get back to fishing. I had the idea of trying it close to the shore, so I took off my beetle spin lure. I worked the tail of my worm lure into the shank of the hook, about to snug it up to the eye of the hook. I stuck myself with the end of the hook, something I almost never do. I slashed the ball of my thumb working the barb loose. I had the anchor down and the river was calm, nothing stronger than slow moving wavelets. Out here on this aluminum boat with no one, entirely on my own—what if I had a heart attack?

Bad things I had done came back to me, back when I was married to Katie. One time Katie showed me a letter from an old boy friend she had before she had Freddie Snipes, and I hit her; I slapped her hard. The river glittering with sunspots, it brought back the sweep of my open hand, the flat pop, Katie's face jerking.

It wasn't long before I hauled up the anchor and dropped the bass I'd caught back in the water. I took the boat back in to the boat dock, and hitched it to the boat trailer. I got in my car and drove to Cole's trailer. Charlene was outside getting her mail. She was flipping through a stack of junk mail. I could tell she wasn't happy to see me show up. She bit her lower lip, turned, and made the strip of carpeting outside the front door. I had to go to her, that's how she wanted it. She set the junk mail on the gas grill, pulled her hip huggers up. Dyan, she told me, was inside watching TV so I couldn't come in.

Right away she had to talk about Cole. "I see you been fishing without Cole?"

"That's right. He says he'd rather paint the church steeple."

"I think it's better that way," she said. Charlene put her hands on her hips, her eyes narrowing like she was going to lecture me, like it was my fault Cole was painting the church. The sun blazed on the blue carpeting. I heard the window unit rumbling, thought it's cool inside but I knew I wouldn't be going inside. Charlene wiggled her toenails, patted one sandal on the carpeting. Her voice, when it came, was distant.

"Look there's something I ought to tell you. About how Cole came to find the Lord."

I slid my feet away, looked at Charlene. "Okay," I said to her, "tell me how Cole came to find the Lord."

Through a gap in the legs of the gas grill, a green lizard crawled past Charlene's toenails, without her seeing it since she was staring at me, crawling inch by inch along the carpeting Cole had tacked down, a cheery sky blue surface for lizards. I was about to stomp on it, would have if it hadn't melted into a shimmying blob.

"Cole's first wife ran off from him. He couldn't get over losing her. He wanted to throw his life away." What Charlene was saying, dwelling on, I knew it meant something to her, but it didn't mean anything to me. "Cole told me he got in his car one day and drove out on County Road One Seventy-Nine. He was going to drive his car into the first big truck he came across. It would have happened, but something else happened instead. Cole saw a little girl on a tricycle, and he forgot about ending his life. He stopped the car right away, and got out—she couldn't have been more than three years old. He asked her where she lived, and she told him. Cole put the tricycle in the back seat and took this little girl home. It was this little girl that saved Cole's life."

It took a lot of concentration, but I made those tufts of blue carpeting come back again, Cole's well-spaced carpet tacks showing forth for me. The lizard had gone its own way. So it was easy for me to say something Charlene would want to hear. "That little girl, who was she?"

"It was the preacher's little girl, at this country church."

"The preacher's little girl. If that isn't something."

"You ask me it was a miracle, Wes."

I thought of Cole up on a ladder, slapping paint on the boards of the squat little steeple that seemed stuck on, not actually nailed down or in some way built, the sun beating down on the back of his neck, Cole painting his way down from the steeple because he thought the Lord wanted him to. I would have said it, where does that leave you and me, Charlene, just to get started again with Charlene, make her feel like having sex with me was okay, but I couldn't speak,

I couldn't even move. Sunspots flashed on the gas grill. I couldn't blink the green blob away.

I didn't have sex with Charlene that afternoon. I spent the afternoon in my trailer with a cold wash rag on my forehead. I watched the Braves lose to the Marlins. In the seventh inning I remembered the date, July 25th. Today, not tomorrow, was my son Tommy's birthday. I had sent him a present, a Tinker toy set, and a birthday card in time for both to get there. He was four years old but I had forgotten, not that he would soon be four years old, I had forgotten today was the twenty-fifth, not the twenty-fourth.

I turned off the TV and picked up the telephone and called Katie, but all I got was a busy signal. An hour later I called again. All I got was the answering machine. I told myself I would call later. I told myself I would get in my car and drive down to Valdosta tonight.

Once the sun went down and it cooled off outside, I left my place and walked over to Elinor's. I knocked but she didn't come to the door. I heard her tell me to come on in. She was sitting in her favorite chair, by the bookcase in front of the television set. She was listening to the radio. The radio was turned down low, and the music was soft, music for dancing I said to myself, only I didn't feel like dancing. She had the lights off, her book in her lap. A mug of black coffee sat close at hand, on a low wicker table in front of her. She had positioned a chair beside her, for me.

"There's a can of beer in the fridge if you want one."

I didn't want one, not tonight.

There wasn't much light in the trailer. A moth lit on Elinor's novel, then spiraled on up to the ceiling light as if it had been caught in a tornado. Mr. Hardcastle, I got to thinking of him again. Had the same wind that blew him around blown the moth up to the ceiling light? But that couldn't be, except in my mind. I remembered this old man I used to see when I lived in Birmingham. This old man was vigorous for his age. He turned up all over the city. That's how this old man spent his life, moving from one public place to another, hospitals, the public library, city parks. He had a bald head and a gray beard, and in warm weather he wore his shirt sleeves rolled up.

The books in the bookcase, the bindings were running together so I had to look back at Elinor. I saw her clearly for a little while, closing her book, marking her place with a bookmark. She picked the mug up with both hands, sipped on the coffee, set the mug back down, her hands jittering from the effort.

"This thing with Charlene, it's doing things to my eyesight."

155

"Your eyesight isn't your problem." Elinor turned off the radio. She moved her chair close to mine. "Your shiftless way of life, that's your problem."

"Shiftless is how I have to live."

"You have to do better than that."

Fork tines, I felt them scratching my eyes. My left eye was burning, specks jittering, zigzagging floaters speeding up. Floaters, that's all they were, no way I would go blind.

"You can change, Wesley. You can be a new man."

A new man, like Cole Hoskins on Highway 179, saving that little girl on a tricycle? I'd just as soon stay like I was, but that wasn't helping any. Sooner or later tonight I'd have to go back to my place. I might go in the other direction first, go past Cole's trailer and on to the river. I'd take off my clothes and jump in, swim upstream, against the current, let the current carry me back. I felt the floaters settle like sand in a pool; they would go away pretty soon. All I had to do was get out of Elinor's chair, do something, keep on the move.

Elinor took my hands in hers. This woman half again my age, I didn't want her to let go of my hands. That's when I got down on my knees and thanked her for believing I could change. That's how the wind was blowing for me.

# Fred, the Hired Hand
## by Bob Sanders

I remember Fred. I've thought about him more lately, especially since this fellow Roden and I were solving some of the world's problems over a cup of coffee one fine day awhile back and ruminating about changes that have taken place over the last few decades.

Yep, I remember Fred, although for the life of me I can't remember his last name. Come to think of it, I'm not certain I ever knew it. It may have been Jones, I'm not sure. Old Fred was Uncle Kelley's hired hand for a period of a couple or three years, along about the same time that Warren Rainwater (or Clyde Turner or Charlie) was working for us. I forget the exact time period.

I learned a lot from Fred. He was my buddy. Looking back on it I don't expect that Fred was anywhere near the genius level in the I.Q. department, but he knew enough to get along pretty well with Kelley's fool mule, Ider. Fred could get a bridle on her—finally, after much soft coaxing—when she'd be in one of her whirling, difficult moods, which was most of the time.

He could talk to fish very convincingly too, sitting on the bridge over Little Yellow Creek, down below Early Matthews' place. His talking didn't result in all that many fish being caught, but he did it well, professionally. It convinced me, at least. Then, when after a great one of those little transparent bluegills would summon up enough strength to make a weak attack on the bait and get itself impaled on the hook, Fred would snort, contemptuously, "Huh! Bite my hook! Think I won't catch you? Huh!"

He courted a good deal, and I was an eager listener to any of the details he cared to reveal to me. Courting seemed more colorful, the way Fred told it, than it did to me several years later when I began to investigate, timidly, that new field of endeavor.

At first, anyway. Fred lived in a converted smoke house right across a public but small road from Grandma Sanders' kitchen. His quarters were small but sufficient, very cozy, in fact. Fred ate the same good food, at the same time, in the same scrubbed kitchen as Kelley, who was a bachelor, and Grandma. However, since he was black, he ate at a little side table while Kelley and Grandma ate at the big table, as did I when I happened to be there at meal time, which was pretty often. The tables were close enough that the vittles and the easy conversation could be handily passed back and forth, and a warm family atmosphere would prevail even while the rigid rules of segregation, albeit separate-but-equal, were being scrupulously observed. For Fred to have taken one step and sat down at the big table would have constituted blasphemy of the very first degree. It was a step of such awesome proportions that I'm quite sure the possibility was never even remotely considered by either Fred or his employers; and so ingrained was the system that nobody even noticed its ludicrousness.

Sometimes when Fred would go to town to court I'd go with him to go to the picture show. I'd cross the road to his place, quietly, and put my eye up to a knot hole in the door and watch him primp for a moment before he'd finally see my eye. He'd look scared for a second—mainly to please me after the first time or two I'm sure—and then let me in.

We'd separate when we'd get to the theater. I'd go downstairs to the main auditorium, and he, after he'd rounded up a girlfriend, if he could find one that night, would go up the stairs to the balcony, where I'd go, after the show got back around to where I came in, to wait for him. While we'd be walking home across the Mile Reed Branch bottom in the pitch blackness, Fred would tell me, from his naturally camouflaged state, that he'd run off and leave me if something jumped out on us. I didn't worry 'cause I didn't believe him … much.

One time we were at the barn, unharnessing old Ider or something, when Fred asked me if I'd seen Simon, who sharecropped up on Mr. Cebe Reeves' place, just up the road. "Oh, I saw some niggers go by a little bit ago," I said.

"What'd you call them?" he asked, not angrily, but with an expression mostly of amusement, with perhaps a tiny trace of hurt in there somewhere—an expression that lingers in the memory.

"Niggers," I said, very softly, hoping the soft mixture of hay and dried manure in the barn's hallway would somehow swallow me up. It was, I think, the hardest word I ever said.

Fred laughed and started telling some crazy tale about old Ider or something, and the incident was soon almost forgotten. Almost. It made a lasting impression, though. Enough that I've never once, since then, used that word, except in quotes. And for that, Fred, old friend, wherever you are, I thank you.

# Dandelion Wishes

by Helen Silverstein

Once in a great while, the sky opens up wide and blue and a lovely breeze finds its way through all that heat, making sunshine your fine companion, warming your skin just right, so that you move out from the shade of the trees right into the giant meadow and begin picking flowers with your best friend in the whole wide world. You can feel the earth, warm and red beneath your feet, still caked hard from the summer's heat, but for today, maybe just for today, your feet don't burn. There's a nice warmth between your toes in the mix of red earth and scratchy green meadow grass. Then you sit down with your best friend, with your pile of yellow dandelions spread out on your lap and you make a fine chain. Yours is really good, 'cause you learned how last year. The breeze moves through your hair and you look up and catch your friend's smile. Her dandelion chain is a mile long at least, and you know she's attached a real important wish to each link, as you have. You hope with all your heart that her every wish comes true. And, though you are old enough to know this won't happen, for this one moment you believe it might. Then your friend leans in toward you and whispers real close to your ear, "Did you know that in heaven one fine moment lasts forever? Did you know?" You shake your head no. Never heard of such a thing. But it may be true, 'cause your friend's dad is a preacher, so she would know. Probably. So you smile, until your stomach turns and you want to ask, does it ever get mixed up in heaven, where a bad moment never ends? But you don't ask, because some things it's better not to know.

# Murder of Crows

## by Jennifer Soule

The vine in a sweet gum tree
moves with the life and sounds
of a murder of crows. A fable
says the phrase derives
from crows gathering to kill
a weak or sickly comrade.
Some speculate it's because
crows feed on carrion, frequenters
of places of death. To Native Americans
the Crow omens a change.
Crow does not inhabit time—
past, present, and future all one.
Yesterday they ganged up
on one bird. But it was a short fight.
They all flew off. The day darkens
with tornado sirens. No partying
like geese on the Chesapeake—
laughing all night drunk on corn.

Today the murder of crows swing
on branches, feast on berries. Dionysian,
berries plucked from the vine—
brawling in the sweet gum and pine.
No tornado warnings. No murder.

# Old Men
## by Peggy Stelpflug

I love old men,
Their deliberateness,
Their quiet charm.

I love old men
Who hold their humor
In their eyes, and
Their wisdom in their thoughts,
Willing to let others learn
The way they did—
On their own,
Trial and error—
The hard way.

I love old men
Who look ahead,
Carefully considering
Each step:
Closing the curtains
At dusk,
Turning off the lights
At bedtime,
Checking the locks
On the doors.

I love old men
Who face death
Matter-of-factly
Like preparing for bad weather,
Knowing there's not much
To do about it
But batten down the hatches,
Just in case …
Zipping their jackets tightly
About their throats

# Hold Promise Over Tomorrow

by Kyes Stevens

last light
on a mountain
home to rebellion
to the senses looking only
at a beating heart

an American Toad
eats roaches
from the cabin
I toss to him
under the light
his front legs folded
waiting             patient

his throat pulses
my heart aches
the way of living
you miss the dead

# Henry
## by Oxford Stroud

Henry is the best liar in Wilcox County. God creates good liars like he creates county agents—one to a county. Everyone in Wilcox has some knowledge of his lie-telling virtue. By that I mean few of us that live happy, adjusted lives ever escape trying to transplant a possibility of truth in the soil of falsehood. But Henry was more than a good liar; he was an artist. Some folks in my section of Wilcox go to church too much; they think telling lies is a sin. They wouldn't know the devil without his forked tail, and if hell isn't hot like the Bible says, some of them won't know when they get there. It's like I say, Henry is an artist, a creator.

His full name is Henry Whittler. I suppose Henry has been the champion of more unusual situations than anyone else in the Western hemisphere. The most wonderful thing about him is that he has never been known to tell the truth, at least not right out loud where most folks could tell it. Henry would say after he ran a finished absurdity of his mental assembly line, "By God, it's the truth; ask my brother Pat." So help me, the only thing that keeps Pat from being a bigger liar than Henry is because Henry got a ten-and-a-half month start on Pat forty-two years ago. No one ever asks Pat any questions. If a liar can't hold up his own tale then he'd better keep it to himself.

As a boy I used to hunt rabbits and quail, mostly squirrels, with Henry. He knew where they all lived. He knew their range, where they got feed and water. He knew what they ate and when they ate it. We always killed game. I learned early that Henry was what most folks call a damn liar, but not too early. It wasn't until I was old enough to be weaned off of smoking rabbit tobacco that I found out that cockle burrs were not really porcupine eggs. For a month and six days a bewildered but faithful hen sat on three smooth white stones and twenty-eight cockle burrs with nothing to show for it but a run-down condition and a tail full of cockle burr quills. After her such patient endurance I was chicken-hearted myself so I went to town and bought a half-dozen chicks and gave them to the feathered mother who was so long over-due. She raised her flock, but she was never the same. Maybe she was old or something.

As I say, I already knew what manner of man Henry was, but it wasn't until later that I found to what degree. It was a late fall day, Saturday afternoon; all the crops were in and the hunting season was still a few weeks down the road.

During these days men folks have more time to chew tobacco and spit on the stove, to sit around the local pool hall and bat the breeze, or, maybe, play a few games of dominoes, or just sit until they had to go home to their old ladies.

The poolroom isn't exactly like a city billiard parlor—no beer, no zootsuited poolroom commando to suck you in for a few games of nine-ball and your pocketbook. Wilcox County is an area of conservative manners, and it's "dry" in a legislative sort of way. I don't say this makes it a better poolroom, only different.

The poolroom was busy this Saturday afternoon and a trifle chilly. I still had my summer's blood so I maneuvered my way into the domino room in search of a warm spot. The spiritual atmosphere I found was as congenial as the room temperature so I parked my sitter on the edge of the wood box. The little pot-bellied stove in the middle of the floor was red around the waist and was putting out as many BTU's of heat energy as an overgrown tom cat during courting season. Of course, if the room gets too hot you can always kick the door ajar, but that's for the house boy to worry about. Hell, you can't play dominoes and worry about the elements too. The game had grown into a conversation.

The conversers were a select group. They weren't of the same social group, that is, they weren't socially equal by strict definition. Most men unlike most women have the freedom to gravitate to a realm of true fellowship if they want to. The conversation was changing directions so I didn't feel left out even though I wasn't being noticed.

"Well, Henry," D.J. asked (D.J. is a man who calls a spade a spade), "when are you going to admit that you stold that prize watermelon? I've seen that gravel pit you live in, and God knows there's not enough nourishment in four cubic yards of that gully dirt to give an earthworm heartburn." Henry, I suppose, had raised the biggest watermelon in Wilcox that year; at least, he said he raised it—a hundred-thirty-seven-and-one-half pounds of watermelon and all under one watermelon rind. "Ask Pat," he would say if anyone doubted that it had come from his land.

"It's not so bad to steal a watermelon but to raffle it off at twenty-five cents a chance is double-jointed dishonesty." John Howard was just out of law school. It was like him to say something like that. Henry had stacked twelve dominoes in a pile and was reaching for the thirteenth. John pushed his chair back from the domino table and wrapping his next words in a cloud of cigaret smoke he continued, "Damn if I don't think you ought to take those seventy-five rocks you made off the illegitimate melon and put it in the town treasury or give it to the church; redeem yourself, Henry, for God's sake."

Everyone had taken part in the case of Henry with their facial expression if not in words. Henry pushed over the stack of dominoes and leaned forward over the table. He looked like a turkey with his long brown neck and red chinless head.

"Where'n hell is Pat?" one of the domino players shouted before Henry could open his mouth. "He'll never get through this one without Pat."

"It's all in knowing how to fertilize your land," Henry said without looking at anyone in particular and at everybody in general. Henry had more time to talk than anybody. He always let his words walk out of his mouth. "The county agent was down home last week, coat, tie, and all trying to pull some of his school-housing on me. He said something about how I ought to work my land under my crop this year, but you can't tell a county agent nothing. He's so damn full of numbers, and charts, and programs, and God knows what else, that he forgets that the ground's got anything to do with farming."

"Henry, don't tell us you used barnyard manure under those watermelons." D. J. had a way of getting down to the raw truth. "I've seen that anemic looking mule you've got, and anything that hayrack left in the barnyard would destroy plant life." Henry must have known that a fragment of truth existed in D.J.'s statement. Actually, Henry's mule had seen his best cotton furrows.

Smiles ranged wide and mellow upon all faces except Henry's. Henry seldom smiles. He never frowns. With him everything is always a proposition of fact or falsehood. There is no American display of teeth and laughter with Henry, but I suspect Henry smiles in his heart; I'd bet on it.

"Go ahead and make fun of Roosevelt if you want to," (Roosevelt, that's Henry's mule). Henry paused, lighting a cigaret, then continued. "But there ain't a damn domino player here that's grown a watermelon that would make my melon a proud step-daddy," he said, recovering the pride that Roosevelt had caused him to lose. "Of course, I really can't take the credit; I'm gonna be honest with you 'cause it's like you say, my land ain't good for growing watermelons. But it all comes with using the right kind of fertilizer." Henry inhaled a cloud of cigaret smoke and let it out in a grey stream across the domino table before he finished speaking, "and you can't find a better fertilizer than ant fertilizer." Although Henry had never been known to tell the truth, he had never been caught with disapproving evidence. For instance, no one could prove that he did not use ant fertilizer under his watermelons.

"Now that's a logical thing to say," John Howard broke in. "Ants have cows; they milk them; why not turn out the ants' milk cows and let them graze under the watermelon vines? Kelly would approve that." Henry wasn't in school the day they learned about ants having milk cows. "There's a sandy hill back of my place," Henry began. "I reckon it's been there for a thousand years or more. It ain't never been good for nothing." Henry always begins speaking in second gear. Most people give a gesture before speaking, say what they have in mind, then become enthusiastic over its possible effect upon the listeners. Henry starts with the second stage and ends there. He says what he has in mind. "I used to wonder why God put that old hill back of my place. I ain't never seen a rabbit track or snake trail across it. It just sits there and looks square at the sun and weather; there ain't even a bush for a thrush to sit on. Things is got a purpose, I always say. I never thought God would build a hill for nothing. Sure 'nuff, the other day I just happened by the old sand hill and you never saw such a sight in your life." Henry held his cigaret between his thumb and forefinger and knocked the ash to the floor with his little finger.

"By damn, I never thought I'd see such a sight on a sand hill. It was just like all these years it had been good for nothing and now it has a purpose. Ants! Great Zion! You've never seen so many ants! I reckon every kind of ant God made was living right there on that sand hill—big black ants, little black ants, big red ants, little red ants, striped ants, grey ants, ants I ain't never seen before, and they was all living just like a big happy family—living and digging and each one going about his own business. I just looked at all those little crawling critters and said to myself, now wouldn't it be a good thing if folks in Camden could carry on like that, nobody stepping on nobody's toes, and everybody minding his own business, and everybody happy with his own load."

Henry's cigaret became too short to hold in his fingers, so he put it in his mouth taking one long last drag and leaning his head aside he puckered his lips and let the butt fall to the floor. No one interrupted him. "Now I'm going to be honest with you," Henry said, glancing up at the domino players. He continued; a sentimental note seemed to hang to his tongue. "I was sorta touched by all those little dirt diggers. I don't know why exactly, but somehow I just wondered how something so small and without no book sense could keep out of trouble." The edge of the wood box was cutting into my breeches so I let my hind end drop down on top of the lumpy, uneven fuel pile, leaving my feet to dangle some inches from the floor. "It ain't like me to take up my time looking at ants," Henry said, "and I don't go round telling just everybody about it, but this is something different. I was wishing somebody had studied ants could of seen all that crawling mess. He could have wrote a book and said things what ain't never been said about ants."

166

"A hellova lot that's got to do with ant fertilizer," D.J. said. There was a thoughtful pause. "Henry, you're just a damn liar," D. J. said hurriedly, then laughed because anyone in the domino room could be called a damn liar without branding another's good nature.

Henry was unaffected. "Well, I got so interested in those ants 'til after while I sat down right in the middle of 'em and began looking at 'em close. I reckon it must have been a gillion of 'em—all kinds. They didn't even notice me. They was crawling all under me and around me. They must have been thinking about something else besides me cause they were running to and fro in single file, half of 'em carrying something in their mouths and half of 'em going to get something to carry. Every once in a spell two of 'em would meet head on—sorta like they was passing the time of day—then run on about their business. I reckon I watched 'em for an hour or more. Then I noticed one little fellow trying to pack a whole dead butterfly. Ants are strong little critters. The little ant would pick up the head of the butterfly and turn it round clockwise, but he couldn't get the butterfly's tail off the ground. Then he would run around and pick up his tail and turn it round counterclockwise, but he couldn't get the butterfly's head off the ground. Then he tried to pick it all up, body, wings, and everything. He strained like hell, but he couldn't do no good. I was wondering how long it was going to take him to try to drag the butterfly. He knew blame well he couldn't tote it. It didn't take long 'cause he soon ran to the head again and grabbed the butterfly by the eyebrows and rared back. I felt sorry for the little fellow knocking himself out over that big butterfly so I figured the least I could do would be to help him along. I picked up a little stick and just as easy as I could, I moved the butterfly up about a quarter of an inch. I really felt like I was doing a good thing. Well, by God, the little ant turned loose the butterfly and started running 'round and 'round like he was crazy or something. I didn't know what to do. I pushed the butterfly back where he'd been, but that didn't do no good. He was running wild—running over little sticks and rocks, and all on top of the butterfly. He just kept on running 'til another ant his size came along and he ran right over him. I don't suppose this ant knew that I'd caused all the trouble 'cause he got mad as hell with him. Then both of 'em tangled up. They was fighting and biting something awful. I felt bad 'cause I'd started all the trouble. I thought maybe I'd break it up so I took a straw and tried to separate them. I learned me a lesson about meddling around with other folks' business right then. You know, no sooner then I got them two ants apart they went and jumped on a big black ant, just like they didn't know what they was doing. The black ant didn't take no foolishness. He made quick work of the two little fellows. I suppose that would have been all there was to it if one of the big red ants hadn't of seen what happened. Now I'm here to tell you, the war started. With this, the big red ants and the big black ants went to war, and all the little ants was getting stomped to death. Ants seemed to come from everywhere. Before I knew what was happening they was all over me and stinging the fire out of me. I ran back shaking the little hot devils off me and hollering and cussing like I ain't never done before. When I stopped and looked around every ant on the sand hill was fighting. There was even more ants than I thought there was, and they was all sounding off—sounded like a bee-hive or something. I reckon I never felt quite as bad as I felt that day. After a while the buzzing stopped and I went back to the ant bed. It was a shame." Henry finally stopped talking for a second and hung his head as if the sins of the world were his alone. It was a good pause. It gave D. J. time to glance at lawyer John and decide whether to smile now or later, or whether to smile at all. No one had seen me sitting in the wood box. Henry assumed the position of speaking more slowly than usual. He drew in two lungs of air and pushed his eye target above the heads of the domino players to the ceiling. Henry said reverently, "There wasn't an ant left alive on the sand hill. The next day me and Roosevelt hauled four wagon-loads of dead ants and buried 'em where I planted my watermelons." Henry got up from the domino table and started crawling into his lumberjacket. It was almost dark, and Henry had to feed Roosevelt, and the hogs, and, what's more, Henry had to go home to his old lady. Before Henry had buttoned his jacket, the smiles of the domino players had waxed into laughter. I pulled myself out the wood box and laughed too.

As I followed Henry to the door someone shouted above the laughter, "Henry, you're just a damn liar!"

"By God, it's the truth; ask my brother Pat." That's all Henry said.

# Any Given Saturday

## by John Summerfield

Everything seems to be a football game or
tailgating and drinking—
an old infirm man in the laundry mat quotes
statistics for all of the SEC's running backs
yet has never read a single poem, or so he says—
my only pair of jeans, my favorite pillow, and three
shirts with grease stains
go round and round like a kung-fu fighter
on a television screen, or an orange
peel knifed off at the pulp
like Gio's granddad did with his fingers—
mirage
a rhyme for orange
orange mirage, my peach-colored shirt,
soaked and sudsy, the smoothed combed Egyptian cotton reminds me of Charlie
Pell and Ode to the Gators, and
I wonder why I know this, and
then I wonder who's winning the game that the old man
listens to on his transistor, and
as the machine puts me into a trance
rain rolls down the road inside tiny aqueducts of concrete
like the big ones that drape the landscape in Sicily
and feed farmland as it did during the Roman Empire, and then I can hear
screams from the large concrete stadium
on Donahue
completely in step with the old man's jumps—
between the machines, he dances.

# Hidden Treasure
## by Amber Tidwell

I am from a small town in Alabama where Southern culture is often honored and sustained in the aged and enduring. Victorian style houses with wrap-around porches, respect for the elderly, and close-knit relationships with kinfolk set the stage for tradition in the small towns of the South. Grandma's house is the center of life, breathed in by family gatherings and secret fried chicken recipes. While I longed to take part in such important rituals, my family never quite pulled off those picture perfect examples. In fact, I had a very different experience with my grandparents that left me a little resentful and unable fully to immerse myself in the fullness of the Southern culture that surrounded me.

For the first six months or so of my fifth-grade year, both of my parents had jobs that prevented them from being home with me after school. Because they couldn't afford an afterschool program, they decided that I would walk each afternoon to my grandparents' apartment until one of them could come pick me up. The thought of having this small bit of independence! To be a walker! Oh, the freedom! I imagined myself standing tall while I waited to cross the road. I followed the path to the apartment in my head, smiling as I walked it. And then, I envisioned my destination and swallowed hard. It wasn't a place I wanted to go.

When the bell rang on the first afternoon, most of the kids at Pepperell Elementary School walked home in groups to the neighborhoods behind the school. However, I was given a special teacher escort to walk me across the dangerous five-lane Opelika Road. Once across, I was on my own to face the sticky dried grass and thigh-high thorny bushes.

Though the walk to the old apartment complex wasn't a long one, it was a scary one. I walked against the traffic on a small path that had no doubt been worn by hitchhikers and braver kids than I. Kids who were most likely headed for trouble and not to their grandparents'. Each passing car made my heart pound with the fear that I would be sucked into its path. I carefully negotiated every single step over old beer cans and onto uneven earth, all the while praying that I would not end up in the deep ditch never to be heard from again.

When I finally arrived at the apartment door, I placed my hand on the slightly dented brass knob situated loosely on the paintbrush-streaked door. I took a dramatically deep breath and pushed against the door that seemed as reluctant to be opened as I was to enter the apartment.

The smell of the kitchen met me first. This first minute was the hardest part of the afternoon routine. I had to breathe, cough, and blink through a reflexive gag before adjusting to the odor. A mixture of spoiled milk and cigarette smoke was always in the air, the base note of the concoction of smells. The next layer of smells varied depending on what had been eaten that day. Often it was the sour and briny smell of saucepans left dirty in the sink. Other times it was watered-down stews going bad in room-temperature pots on the stove. Always the smells were unbearable.

I hurried through the kitchen and announced my arrival. The television was so loud that I knew they had not heard the door open or my gags. Bands of dusty sunlight peeked in through the broken and unevenly lowered blinds that hung in the only windows in the front part of the apartment. The angle of the sun during the afternoon spotlighted the line-up of twenty or more plastic translucent orange pill bottles sitting in the windowsill. Each day I made a point to kiss my grandmother on her bristly face. She sat on a pumpkin-orange couch that was upholstered in what looked and felt like burlap. Most of the couch was covered by her body which was dressed in one of her many bright colored flowery muumuus. The rest of the couch and her legs were covered in a worn afghan that was crocheted in a zigzag pattern alternating pastel yellow and pine green. She smiled kindly at me each afternoon.

My grandfather sat in a dark brown vinyl recliner lined with thin towels. His sweaty black hair was greasy and his bangs stuck to his forehead. Though his eyes never connected with me, he would sometimes mumble a hello through his barely parted lips. He made me feel anxious, as if he was waiting for me to get into trouble. With my clumsy lanky body, I could only fulfill his expectation. I tried to balance avoiding him altogether and the urge to show him that I was a good girl.

I usually spent the first twenty minutes of my time there refilling their drinks, checking their mail, and completing other tasks they had not done during the day. Once these small chores were done, it was my job to sit still. The room was small and sparsely furnished. The only seat for me was right beside the television, which meant that I couldn't see it. I could have settled on the floor, but the matted tan carpet was littered with chip and cookie crumbs. The thought of my palms and legs grinding into the dirty floor was enough to keep me still in my chair. Besides that, they watched court shows and I wasn't the least bit interested in the drama of adults with their stolen garden hoses and broken promises.

I sighed and fidgeted in my chair, marking time by whatever show was on. I held my backpack between my dangling feet as if to protect it. I played with my blonde split ends. I stared at my grandparents for minutes at a time. These two people who made my father. My mother's parents died when she was just a little girl. I heard stories from her about how they were not very good people, and with those stories so went the fantasy that maybe they were really the grandparents I longed for. The two people in that room with their numb and slightly irritated expressions were my only hope for the special connection I'd observed on sitcoms and heard about from school friends. I longed for a tender relationship with them.

My grandmother was once a woman of adventure, but I only knew her as diabetic, overweight, and unable to walk without a walker. While drifting in and out of sleep on the scratchy couch, she would often wince and gasp. I looked at her and my stomach did flips. She seemed to be in constant pain.

I called her "Maw." My grandfather was "Nan." As the oldest grandchild in the family, it was my earliest strained syllables that named them. And as all nicknames do, these communicated an endearing and hopeful affection. As I grew older, I realized that these names didn't mean much of anything to any of us. They were just the words used to get a person's attention or to casually mention them in conversation.

On that first awkward afternoon at their apartment and maybe for the first week, I tried desperately to engage them in conversation. I wanted to tell them about my day but their signals to me were clear; I was shushed even during the commercials. On a few occasions I was brave enough to duck out of the room and venture into the bathroom where I lingered over celebrity tabloids or to the bedroom where I played with my grandmother's jewelry.

The jewelry was the best part of being there. The first time I opened the dirty white box the inside took me by surprise. Each separated compartment was lined with light blue velvet. The sections housed clip-on earrings that had lost their snap, tarnished and twisted chains and faux pearl necklaces that dangled to my knees. I dressed myself up in these treasures and made silent promises to myself to be famous enough to wear the real versions someday. Before taking them off, I would swirl around until I felt the weight of necklaces swing out from my body and then brace myself as they clacked back against my chest. The noise was usually my grandfather's cue to call me back into the living room. His booming voice triggered my fear and hustle, and I quickly ripped off the jewelry and placed it back in the box.

One Friday night my cousin Sally and I spent the night at their apartment. We were excited at the prospect of a night away from our parents. We giggled and talked in whispers after they were in bed and explored curious drawers that were off limits during daylight hours. As the night passed, we decided to make breakfast for them as a thank-you for letting us stay the night.

We crept into the kitchen and found pans, a toaster, eggs, milk, orange juice, coffee, and margarine. The sun started to peek in through the dusty windows as we assembled ingredients along the crowded counter. Sally was busy making the toast. I focused on the eggs, trying not to get any of the shell in them like my mom taught me.

That's when I smelt smoke. I quickly turned toward Sally who was waving smoke away from the toaster, doing her best to make it go away. The smoke billowed and the bread burned. There was nothing we could do to stop it, and that's when the smoke alarm went off.

We heard Nan shout obscenities from the back bedroom. I glanced around in fear, not sure what to do. Sally hid under the kitchen table. When Nan rounded the corner and saw the mess we'd made, he yelled at us and cursed at the smoke. His voice was louder than the beep of the smoke alarm. He commanded us out of the kitchen and back to bed. My heart pounded for almost an hour after the incident, but the sounds of his anger lingered in my ear for years.

By the time I was in high school, both of my grandparents were dead. The last time I visited Maw in the hospital, my mouth tasted like metal and the sight of bright cold silver and sea green tiles made my teeth hurt and my stomach turn. Both of her legs had been amputated. I kissed her face and tried not to stare at her bandaged stubs. A few days later she was dead. At the funeral I remember the bottom half of the coffin covered her legs, or where her legs would have been, like a cold metallic afghan. I missed her for a while after that. Hers was my first experience with death. When Nan died, I was away at a band competition and unable to attend his funeral. I didn't even cry.

It took me a while to realize that not all grandparents were like mine. My friend Jill's grandmother owned a farm and saddled horses for us to ride on the weekends. She waterskied and drove the boat when we went to the lake. There's even a legendary story about the time she killed a chicken with her bare hands. Amy's grandmother and grandfather were her biggest fans. They visited at holidays and for band concerts and brought presents with each visit. Even Michelle, whose grandparents were in poor health, talked regularly to them on the phone, and mourned a great loss at the death of her grandmother a few years ago.

The visual of the white-haired sharing strong wisdom and sweet affection with younger generations is a prevailing theme in most stories revolving around family, especially in the South. Sometimes I feel slighted that I missed out on one of the most celebrated relationships in Southern culture. Most of the time I am barely aware of the deep resentment I carry over this until it shows up in my aversion to the elderly, stew, and cheap vinyl reclining chairs. I find myself staring curiously at toddlers greeted by their teddy-bear grandparents and I often tease my friends who drop everything once a month to make visits out of town. I like to think of myself as a person of experience, emotionally equipped for things in life that come my way, but the older I get, the more I realize that I am truly at a loss when it comes to relating to people in this area of life. They sit around and talk about the silly and sweet things their grandparents do while I silently watch.

A few months ago during a cross-country move, I found some old pictures. There was one of me and Maw at Lake Martin. We were both crouched down on the ground and we both had small stones in our hands. I saw the picture and I remembered that we used to explore things together. We walked the dirt lake roads and dug through the mud, all because Maw convinced me that there was a treasure to be found. We walked through the woods and she showed me unusual plants and birds while she told me stories of snake bites and trips to Pike's Peak. On one walk she let me eat a cherry tomato right off the vine. In the picture we are both smiling. I pulled it out of the pile of photos and put it in my Bible.

# The Old Man and the Tree

## by Christy Truitt

I masked a grimace as I winched out of my son's convertible. Tin can described it better. Who would pay more for a car than I ever made in a year? And with the top-half gone? My first-born child, that's who. Sheesh—no wonder his generation's squandering Social Security.

Another thing I wouldn't have to worry about. I'd run out long before Social Security. Cancer made sure of that.

"Come on, Grandpa. I wanna see the tree. They say it ain't gonna be here much longer. I ain't never seen no dying tree! Have you?" Oscar's words were one, long, run-on sentence.

He rambled out of earshot as his dad chased after him. Lucky he didn't end up a squirrel under some fool's tire. I righted my walking cane, buttoned the top of the trench coat, and hobbled my way to a corner bench. The wind stirred some leftover toilet paper, whisking it around my head, bringing back the memory.

"Will you marry me?" Scariest four words I'd ever uttered. She must not have heard me from the swell of students celebrating Auburn's basketball victory. Maybe it was a sign not to say it again. God protecting me from rejection. Our parents said we were too young anyway. "Boy, you hadn't even graduated high school. How you gonna provide for a family?" my dad had shouted over a whiskey tumbler.

I leaned closer, cupping my mouth against her ear. "I said, will you marry me?!!"

Lillian stood before me in a straight skirt down to her knees, my high school letterman's sweater swallowing her thin shoulders. I'd given it to her the year before, right after our first kiss. Funny how someone you'd known your whole life became a new person once she settled in your heart.

I liked the new trend in clothes, glad the powers-to-be had ditched the poodle skirts in favor of more form-fitting attire. Lillian's figure sure had changed since we first caught tadpoles at Chewacla Creek all those years ago. The new skirt hugged her new curves.

Her mama 'bout had a fit, saying the devil was behind it. "That Elvis Presley did this. Gyrating and shaking all over the place. Turning good Christian girls into tramps!" Lillian's mama ranked rock-n-roll right up with Crimson Tide football as the root of all evil. "You will NOT walk out of this house in such skanky clothes!"

Like most things, including marrying me, Lillian didn't always mind her mama. Sixty-three years and two boys later, I now sat alone, watching the grandson she never met.

I looked up into the towering oak. "So you're dying, old girl. Well, join the club." I wondered if maybe, just maybe, I could hide in one of the branches. Somewhere high where cancer couldn't find me. They wanted to pump me full of poison to save my life. No thanks, I told 'em. I'd go out on my own terms.

The tree swayed in the wind, tossing a few leaves down on me. "Yeah, I see ya. Sure don't look sick. Guess you'll go on your own terms, too." I'd read the newspapers, watched the television reports. Some fool poisoned the Toomer's oak trees, denying future generations of Auburn fans the tradition of rolling their branches after victories.

The pain seized me for a minute, snatching the breath from the farthest depth of my lungs. I gasped and clutched my stomach. No one noticed. Everyone was too busy taking pictures of the poisoned tree like some freak at the circus. Pretty soon, I'd be just like her. Lying in a hospital bed, visiting with people brave enough to talk to a dying man. Just another old person. Just another tree. Won't mean a thing after a while. We'll both be gone.

Forgotten.

"Grandpa, look!" Oscar's eyes swallowed his face, the color of the summer oak leaves now turned brown. The color of mine.

I took out a handkerchief and dotted my forehead. "What is it, Oscar? Whacha got there?" The kid never noticed how labored the words sounded, the shallow breath. He'd never known me as anything other than old. The oak and I both looked at Oscar, longing for the time we were strong and sturdy.

"It's a baby of the Toomer's oak. The lady over there was selling them. Dad bought me one. Said we could plant it at the farm to make sure the poison didn't kill the oak forever. He said if we took care of the baby, it would grow up just like the Toomer's oak. It would live forever!" Oscar danced around my knees while his blond hair bobbed up and down.

I took my grandson's face in my hands, touching the smooth skin Lillian and I helped create by creating his daddy. I closed my eyes for a moment, his skin becoming his grandmother's, soft and young on that long ago night she said yes. A full-circle moment arrived when I opened my eyes and saw my son leaning against the trunk. He had an inquisitive look on his face, chewing the inside of a cheek like I do when figuring out the Wheel of Fortune puzzle.

Oscar's chocolate eyes shined up at me. He waved the tree in my face, almost taking out an eyeball. I laughed, gesturing for my son to join us. "That's right. The babies carry on the legacy to make sure the oaks aren't forgotten." Poison might kill me and the trees, but our children ensured we'd live on.

My son joined us. "Hey, Dad, how 'bout we walk over for a Toomer's lemonade? Remember how we used to do that when I was little? Oscar's never had one. You can tell him about the time the police brought you home in nothing but your skivvies when you were his age. Bout how my granddaddy whooped you so bad you couldn't sit for a week."

I laughed and ruffled Oscar's hair, forgetting the cancer chomping through my liver. "I'm sure we can think of a few tales to tell. Traditions are important things to carry down, so I'm sure I can remember a few stories about your daddy. Let's go get that lemonade."

I looked up again at the oak. The sun filtered through her branches as if the tree winked at me.

# Dirt Roads
## by Peggy Walls

Dirt roads lead to creeks that rise in spring rains
and to unplowed fields of weed and vine,
where unnamed lanes meander from sight,
bordered with towering trees of oak and pine.
Dirt roads lead to cold, mineral springs,
to weathered porches where swings still hang
abandoned old barns with hay-filled stalls
to open lofts and tin roofs rusting in the rain.
Dirt roads lead to kudzu-covered sites,
where chimneys of stone crumple in place.
When memory takes me down a dirt road,
these are the familiar scenes I retrace.
The wind weaves through an orchard of trees,
near clapboard houses and butterfly fields.
I am welcome still, where concrete ends,
and dirt roads wend into forested hills.

# The Gift from the Hummingbird

by Barabara Wiedemann

The hummingbird
trapped on the enclosed porch
probed the screen with its beak
patiently searching for a way
to the greenery of the trees
to the pink of the crepe myrtle
to the alluring trumpet shape
of the red bloom of the cypress vine.
Over it I cast a linen towel
and for just a moment
I held a hummingbird.
It emitted a high plaintive tone
twice it wailed—
the pure sound of despair.
Outdoors
I opened the cloth
and the hummingbird vanished.

# Halawakee Talking
## by Scott Wilkerson

There is a grist mill on the Halawakee tributary. They used to call it Bean's Mill or just plain Bean's. I'm told it dates from the War of Northern Aggression, which means its memory has been withheld until the archivist at the Riverview Library can review the evidence. All I really know is that the water rises high as myth in spring floods and freezes into transcension come winter. One of those winters, so my father's father told me, the frozen arc of water broke off the fall and floated down as far as the next county, whereupon Sherriff Putney declared a state of amergency (his spelling) and Deacon Virgil Hopkins issued a public prayer "beseeching [a] merciful and unfathomable God for a beneficent and fiscally sustainable end to this natural oddity."

In a letter dated six weeks hence, after what the *Shawmit Daily* (which was in fact a weekly) had named the "waterfall ice-berg" had melted, causing only an unprecedented, but not unwanted, flooding of Osanippa Creek, Deacon Hopkins explained that his use of the term "natural oddity" in his public prayer (reprinted below with permission from the former editors of the now defunct *Shawmit Daily*[sic] was the providential gift of his literary theology in which nothing, not even the beastly not even the odd, is un-natural.

Maud, I have wondered at the shimmering and prismatic flicker of the light through that waterfall. And I'm willing to believe that it has a divine origin just like the Deacon says, but I have to confess that such beauty seems somehow to sweep over Nature and drift a right far ways beyond.

yrhmblsvt,
Felix

## An Ad Hoc Prayer for Mercy

Heavenly Father, we come to you
humble as supplicants in the good old style,
begging your intervening hand in the matter
of this natural oddity that has so griped [sic]
our fair county and its council-approved annexes
in mortal fright.

Stay that mighty iceberg and its shards
and any attendant scrapes of rafts
or barges
or boats carrying perishable inventory to Mobile
or any fishing boats not properly anchored
even though I told Ike Spivey he has to tie
that thing up or else.

Though we do not deserve your help
Any more than we deserve your Love,
We need a dose of both.
Amen

# Growing Up in Auburn: Part 1
## by John M. Williams

Auburn, Alabama—that's my hometown. It's not mine anymore, but from the late fifties through the early seventies it was my and my fellow froglings' pond. I know that many of us, my fellow froglings and I, consider ourselves winners of some cosmic lottery to have been placed there, at the time we were, for the communal drama of our coming-of-age. As a college town, it was buffered from the abyss of small-town hell. Intelligent, educated people were around, big acts occasionally passed through, on certain fall Saturdays the population quadrupled in a bizarre frenzy, and we had liberals. Yet at heart it was still a small, sleepy town whose frontiers, in every direction, quickly surrendered to the rural South.

The fact is, there was a fragile balance. Intelligent people, higher education itself, generate the air of possibility; and sleepy towns force the imagination inward.

The mythic quality of Auburn in my memory, correcting for enhancement, I believe derives from its mythic quality in reality as I grew up there. We created our own world as children, and that must explain why it all still seems so near to me; it was largely within all along.

### Woodfield

I was born in Montgomery, and my family moved to Auburn when I was an infant. My father worked for Alabama Power Company, and when an opening came up in Auburn, he jumped on it. I have always considered this decision critical to the fortunes of our family—it was a move that put us in a position to ascend on that great upward-sloping terrain of middle America.

We settled in on Woodfield Drive, in a flat-roofed, bamboo-plagued, pecan tree-shaded house we rented from the aptly named Mr. Porch. This house and the mystique-drenched yard that surrounded it were my world until I was seven. I cruised those environs in Adamic wonder, as some brooding, protective spirit looked down from above. I had a stick horse that I loved, whose head was a soft stuffed tube with eyes, ears, mane, etc. Other kids had only those little plastic-headed ones that I viewed with the four-year-old version of the emotion that would later ferment into disdain.

A fence ran round the yard, and there were certain spots where I would position myself. Naturally, in my memory I see it all from those perspectives.

At the far back northeast corner I could gaze in one direction to woods that could only have stretched a couple hundred yards to Virginia Avenue, but to me seemed like something worthy of Lewis and Clark; and in the other, to a field exalted with crimson clover in spring, and pecan trees, to the back reaches of the Guytons' house where there were rabbits in wire pens. Professor Guyton, some years Daddy's senior and his fishing buddy, was quite colorful. They don't call you "Goofy" for nothing. I don't even know what he taught, horticulture or something, but I remember my uncle's story about him from when he was in college. A student asked Prof. Guyton how the grade would be determined, and he explained that he would count the main exams such and such a percent, average in the daily quizzes, the classwork, with the labwork counting so much, and "then give you what I damn well please." I remember the day he caught a twelve-pound bass, and how enormous that fish was.

Another favorite spot was on the west side of the yard, by the Graves' house. The fence, square-wire on metal poles, was detached there and habitually collapsed to the ground like a loose sock, and must have been too much trouble to fix because all anybody ever did was yank it back up and prop it on the pole where it stayed about as long as a pulled-up loose sock does. So it was a certified "low place" that I was warned to stay away from. Inevitably, one afternoon I slipped out and headed off into the beguiling unknown. Mama conducted a periodic check and—just that fast!—I had disappeared. Auspiciously, Ginger, my beloved Ginger, half boxer, half blimp, who would snorfle her bowl of food in a single breathtaking spasm of ingestion leaving exactly the polished chopped onion pieces from the salad, was gone as well. Mama (they tell me) went into full panic. Daddy and his co-workers were summoned and the neighborhood combed. I was found in a wooded area up the street by Mr. Straiton, Ginger in faithful attendance. Good ol' Ginger.

I remember riding in the car with Mama. We had a fifty-something Buick I had a bad habit of enlisting as the main prop when I played "gas station man," using sand for gas—even caught, in *flagrante delicto*, in the background of a home movie—and in this pre-seat belt era I would stand on the middle of the bench-seat beside her. At any sudden stop or swerve her guardrail arm would swing over, a reflex she kept as long as she drove, though the toddlers evolved into various chihuahuas and eventually nothing. I can call back the feeling of sitting in the little kid seat on the grocery buggy as Mama went up and down the aisles of the A&P, when it was on South Gay Street. That smell! The produce and Eight O'Clock coffee—which migrated with the store up the street in the mid-sixties, and played evocative havoc with me when I worked there in '69 and '70. I remember Mr. Tidwell (later my boss) and mother-hen cashier Mae MacHargue, (later a chirping scold as I bagged on her checkout lane). Leaving, we would drive around the building, past a belching vent in the narrow alley between the store and a marvelous old house half digested by Southern flora, which upon the death of the inevitable widow became a hippie nest through the early seventies, then at last fell victim to that most distinctive of Auburn traditions: the razing of the old, gracious, and beautiful, and replacing it with the vulgar, tacky, and dreadful.

For a convenience store, in that pre-convenience store world, we had Southside, or as I believed it to be until I learned to read: Sow-side (now The Gnu's Room). I remember the milk coolers in the back, Mr. Wright the butcher, the creaking wooden floors, the front corner of exotica, including snails and (who of us ever forgot?) chocolate-covered ants, the two checkout lanes with towering cigarette racks above the cash registers, and, of course, Mr. Storey, the bustling, congenial proprietor. It was something of a milestone when I got old enough to go in for the milk or bread myself, Mama waiting in the car, and I can remember being puzzled when I had the exact change, because I thought the whole point of going through the line was to get money back.

I can't say how my brother Chuck, three years my senior, dealt with my arrival, with resistance undoubtedly, but when my sister Carol was born when I was four, I remember my feelings of jealousy and resentment. I would go to her crib, with its slowly-twirling songbird mobile, when no one was looking, and pinch her. Okay, that's bad—but sue me, I'm human. I remember my grandmother coming from Notasulga to help Mama, who had her hands full.

Mama. Naturally, the Significant Other of that realm. When I close my eyes and think of her, I see a slideshow of her whole life, all the way to the Parkinson's-ravaged end, but definitively then: twenty-five and beautiful.

That's who I see walking down Mrs. Meagher's bumpy brick driveway the day I started kindergarten. It was the second, after birth itself, of life's serious traumatic experiences. I screamed in all the terror of primordial separation, as Mrs. Meagher said, "I've got him, Mama, go ahead," and held me—pinned me!—as Mama, her face seared with love's anguish, disappeared down the hill. When she came back to get me at noon, I didn't want to leave—so as traumatic experiences go, it was brief. I will never forget Mrs. Meagher, nor her comic handyman husband, Red, nor her schoolmarm bell, nor that little kindergarten room, the green file boxes with our names written on them in nail polish, the apple juice and graham crackers, scissors, paste, and everything else.

184

Nor the playground with its sandboxes and swing sets and monkey bars. That first distressful day, I was given the diversionary task of counting the trains that went by. The tracks passed right behind the kindergarten, not even a block from the station. I forget how many there were, but I do believe that is where I developed my love of trains. To this day I feel a shiver when I hear one, and still watch them pass in awe (I'm one of the few people in the world who considers having to stop for a train a lucky break)—even if they are only freight trains. Because it was the passenger trains, of course, that gave me the thrill. Those blue West Point Route engines—the blue or silver cars with the cool green windows. I can still see them sitting there at the station, hissing and purring, and I remember looking at the profiles of the passengers behind the windows, wondering how anybody could be that lucky. But I don't think I philosophized too much when I became one of those profiles as we rode to Montgomery, then caught the L&N Hummingbird to Mobile to visit our cousins, at how the fulfillment is not only not as good but isn't even the same category of thing as the longing.

Mrs. Meagher held a reunion every year for her high school-graduating alumni, and when our turn came, I had to get special permission to take off a couple of hours from the A&P. Of course, Mr. Tidwell, that Pall Mall-smoking Jackie Gleason-lookalike I can still picture in Santa Claus costume on a fire truck, let me. There's a group photo somewhere. An embarrassingly rich number of those people became lifelong friends.

One more story from the Woodfield days. 1957, a couple of years before we moved. Next door to us lived the Macons. Two slightly older than me, beautiful girls, a mom I don't recall, and the dad, Nat Macon, who was a physicist or mathematician, I'm not sure which. This may have been the first time I heard the word "genius"—which he may have been, or it may have just been blue-collar code for "real smart." He took us out in the yard one night and showed us where to look, and sure enough, right where he pointed, not to mention when, a little star silently sped across the arc of the night sky. Sputnik. I remember when I heard the Russians had shot a dog into space—who wouldn't be coming back!—I pictured Ginger in there all hooked up with tubes and wires, looking out the window, thinking where did they go? The Macons moved soon after that—he to some kind of hot-shotdom in Washington, if memory serves.

## Brookside

When we were building our house on Brookside Drive, almost exactly to the lot a block away, we kids would go down there after hours and snoop around, and play with the lumber scraps, and build little structures of our own. A big water oak stood just behind the house, and towers there to this day, three-pronged and shading the lives of strangers. My God, that I've lived to say that.

I remember vividly the sense of freedom and possibility and immunity from prosecution of childhood. On a typical Saturday morning, if we didn't go to the kids' show at the Tiger Theater for six Golden Flake wrappers and six Coke caps that we would fish out of drink machine receptacles with a magnet on a string, I would rise pretty early, get some breakfast while those early bad generic westerns were on, maybe watch a few cartoons, then meet my pals. My best friend of early childhood, and the barefoot prototype of the genre, was Grady Hawkins—though the "best" umbrella would have to include Sharon Rouse and Wells Warren. In fact, somewhat later, Sharon, Wells, and I comprised the sole membership of the "Three Best Club," a group as tough to crack into as Augusta National. On those mornings, we would often have a debate, which could grow contentious, over how to fill the approximately twenty hours until lunch, not to mention the forty hours after. Sometimes we would draw in the sand of Sharon's driveway, perhaps pick someone to spy on, or put somebody's head in a sack, spin them around, then lead them circuitously to some spot and have them guess where it was—always a mile off. Evenings, we often played Kick the Can, with a ball, squeezing every photon of light out of the day. But mostly we would gravitate toward one of our alter-universes—either the lot sandwiched behind our houses, where we built forts, one of which was Ft. Brooksam (amalgamation of Brookside and Salmon)—later, Brookswam (the "w" for Grady's Woodfield), another, The Professional Nasty Center. I'll leave that to your imagination.

Or we would head down to Gay Street, and Salmon's Pasture.

Professor Salmon, neighborhood mogul, who lived on the corner of Brookside and Wright's Mill, owned all the land around there. I remember him as a brisk, purposeful man in a hat, and Mrs. Salmon, who survived him many years, as a nice enough, but a rather aloof and intimidating lady. He had apparently thought to go into the dairy business at one time, and in the "pasture" stood a silo, a dairy barn, and a big open-sided barn full of agricultural equipment—all of it long abandoned even then. On the end of the dairy barn grew a grove of chinaberry trees, whose green berries made excellent slingshot ammo, a fact which led to the founding of the Slingberry Club and some epic wars. Another entry-point into that world was the raised sewer line on South Gay that you walked, over the creek, to a terminus in the woods. We spent hours, years, in these places, damming the creek, catching crawdads, making purple privet berry juice, building forts, losing ourselves in a cosmic web of make-believe that would seem extraordinary except that it was ordinary. The Vanderbilt Man, a Frankenstein-like figure, roamed these environs, as did The Girls—a tribe of ruthless, Amazonian females with a penchant for capturing and undressing you. You never knew, on any given day, what you might run into.

I attended first through fourth grades at Samford School, then fifth and sixth at brand-new Wright's Mill. My grade school teachers—seven, including Mrs. Meagher—come back to me in a surge of affection. After my family, they are easily the most influential people of my life. I think this is true for many people—so why is the job so lightly regarded? Don't ask me.

Growing up in a college town, one absorbs those rhythms and, I've discovered, never really shakes them. "When the students are gone," "the students are back," the general rise and fall of quarters (now semesters)—these are indelible categories to the natives. Along with that distinctive explosive roar coming across town on Saturday afternoons, and the blare of KA parties at night. And, often poignantly, people moving in and out. During this period our next-door neighbors were the Russells—baby Jay, my pal Rusty, the unforgettable Erk, and Jane, his wife. They ran their window air conditioner year round. Down on South Gay lived the Dooleys—and they all left Auburn for Athens (and Statesboro) and their own fame at the same time. Years later, when I was running a printing business in Auburn, my landlord was Bobby Freeman, who had played at Auburn with Vince Dooley and a little after Erk Russell, and I sat for hours listening to him talk about those days and his later career in the NFL.

While we're at it, a couple more football references—we're talking about Auburn, after all. The year 1963 was a great one for Auburn, and I was a transported, walls-covered-with-newspaper clippings, eleven-year-old fan. My buddy Grady Hawkins and I especially idolized Jimmy Sidle and Tucker Frederickson, and sometimes rode over to the practice field. One day (actually 1964, I believe), we were hanging around there, and went into the Field House on the north end of Cliff Hare Stadium, and were standing in the hall by a water fountain. I will never forget this: out walked, in full pads, number twelve himself—Jimmy Sidle. Mr. Roll-Out. He was huge! He had that famous facial tic. I was speechless, but Grady, braver, asked him how his knee (I think) was doing (he had a recent injury), and Sidle made some polite response, drank some water, and headed out to the field.

We had brushed shoulders with greatness. The news of his death several years ago made me sad.

My friend Bill Beckwith, whose father was Sports Information Director, though I don't think they called it that then, once got me a piece of notebook paper autographed by the entire 1963 team! Sidle, Frederickson, Bucky Waid, Bill Cody, Doc Griffith, Woody Woodall, and all the rest. I've lost it! I've also lost the couple of chin straps I had—those puffy white ones the players wore then and that we stormed the field at the ends of games to get. We had gotten in by selling programs or cokes. I remember the pervasive smell of whiskey and the billion whiskey bottles in the student section. All a thing of the past.

I started delivering newspapers too in the sixth grade, and if I may be indulged in getting ahead of my story just a year or two, when I was throwing *The Birmingham News* one leg of my route was the dreaded upper Woodfield, a steep curving hill which to a kid on a bike loaded like a C-5 was formidable. I had several customers up there, including the Jordans. When I "collected," I dealt with Mrs. Jordan, whom I remember as a warm, cheerful lady, but once, I was ushered into the den to have things squared away by the man of the house. And there he sat, memorabilia around him, basset hound at his feet: Shug. I can't remember what I mumbled, nor what he graciously replied, but I do remember his house shoes.

One of Shug's coaches was Gene Lorendo, whose kids, Cam, Mac (deliberate palindrome? I always wondered), and Leah, were about our age, and whose wife, Jean Lorendo (was that on purpose too?) was my Cub Scout Den Mother. She is one of the most amazing women I ever met—in the world of crafts and hand-work, she could do anything, including carry on a fully-engaged conversation while knitting, without looking, at the speed of light. Amazing. They lived in one of those houses at Graves' Amphitheater, with a gigantic loom on the porch, and two German Shepherds: Vandy and Weagle. Once, they had a litter of puppies and that's where we got our beloved Rex. What a dog. Mama and Daddy were in Sunday school one Sunday morning, a mile away downtown, and a fire truck came by blaring its siren, Rex in full pursuit. He got cancer in his leg when he was only seven or eight, ended up having the leg amputated, and lived another year or so, only a little impeded, with three. When he was very sick I went over to the vet school and got in the cage with him.

JFK got elected President and they said he was the youngest ever at what seemed to me the Methusalean forty-three. Then came the Cuba business and the H-Bomb scare. The A-Bomb was one thing, but the H-Bomb! I remember inspecting a sample bomb shelter at Neal Ingram's Amoco station, and contemplating where in the back yard we could dig the hole to put it. We made lists of what we would need inside there, and along with everybody accepted the grim reality that if anyone tried to get in, you'd have to shoot them. Americans always pull together in a crisis.

Where was I when I heard President Kennedy had been shot? In Mrs. Green's sixth-grade class. Of course, I remember it. She was called out, came back in, hardly able to speak, and told us: "The President has been shot." School was dismissed. For the first few hours the news was that he was in the hospital, they were doing all they could; nobody knew then that the back of his head had been blown off. There followed that surreal sequence of Walter Cronkite, LBJ, Jackie, Oswald, Ruby, funeral cortege with John John walking alongside. None of us suspected, of course, how the world was about to change. My generation seemed primed for the cataclysmic. We absorbed that cataclysm which, like all the ones to follow, became a part of us.

Early the following year we decided we needed nicknames. I remembered a kid from somewhere around there nicknamed "Beetle," and I liked that, so I announced I would henceforth be "Beetle." "Oh-h-h," scoffed Bill Dyas, "trying to be the beetles." The beetles? What was that? The word didn't have an "a" yet. As always, I was the last to know. Of course, I was soon to find out. Like all the other gazillion people, I watched them on Ed Sullivan. I've tried—with students, my own children (both big fans)—to explain it, and I can't. You can adduce all the sociological, psychological, whateverological explanations you want, and there's still no way to account for, or understand, that million-volt thrill that went through you at the sight or sound of them.

Ginger got terminally ill not long after that. The plan was for Mama to take us kids to her sister's in Mobile while Daddy handled the sad business. I remember saying goodbye to Ginger—singing "All My Loving." The words fit too well. My first love song—to a dog. I couldn't bear to listen to that song for many years after that; now it's one of my most beloved: not only does it evoke the memory of Ginger, but it was the first song any of us ever saw the lads play.

If you drive down Gay Street today you will see a silo standing incongruously in a walking park. You will not see the long-lost world that once enveloped it. That world is a ghost, living only in my and a few other people's mental closets. I occasionally pass the place today on a road that didn't exist in my childhood, glance at it, but never feel nostalgic. It's as though the silo had been lifted from its original place, and set down in some other—which in a way it has been. I realized one day, it's not in a different time, but in a different place—in fact, they are the same. Everything is expanding; the world is not where it was. I seek refuge sometimes in that world, but more often in the even older world, the weightless world with its radiant maternal spirit, of Woodfield, and simply float there, drifting from spot to spot. And now I know who was looking down on me the whole time. It wasn't God, or a guardian angel—it was me. Well, maybe that is a sort of guardian angel. I basically agree with Wordsworth: I was closer to the stuff from which all this comes—certainly a spiritual existence, compared to this.

Well, anyway, I believe I've taken the story to 1964. I would be twelve in August—the President had been killed, the Beatles were upon us, and the world would never be the same again.

# SECTION III
Remembering

# Eulogy for Wayne Greenhaw June 4, 2011

## by Wayne Flynt

For the past few days, I pondered what brought Wayne Greenhaw and me (and Bill Baxley for that matter) together today. Different people from different places with different careers. After considerable speculation, I settled on one unifying movement containing many separate parts. Born only a year apart, the three of us left the culture into which we were born during our teenage years and entered through the gates of history into the most powerful freedom movement of the twentieth century. If the Depression and the Second World War defined our parents' generation, the Civil Rights Movement defined ours.

In his last book, *Fighting the Devil in Dixie*, Wayne describes his experiences as a young boy so crippled by infant polio that he underwent major surgery to correct a spine distorted by the disease, followed by nearly a year in a body cast. At first thrown into despair by the pain and isolation, he began to read (the Bible; history; fiction), to pray, and to believe again in the future. Central to his recovery were the ministrations of his beloved Presbyterian pastor in Tuscaloosa who brought him comfort and hope. But that same pastor in later years invited Stillman College faculty to their church, thus alienating many parishioners, including some of Wayne's relatives. The minister was replaced, and the disillusioned teenager began a journey toward a different kind of faith.

As with many human tragedies, Wayne's polio and long recuperation drove him into an imaginary world of books which can transport us beyond present reality. One world he discovered that he would soon transform from imagination to concrete reality was the Writers' Workshop in San Miguel de Allende, Mexico. After graduating high school, he boarded a train for the land of the Aztecs and Toltecs (Mayans), where he learned to write, to speak Spanish (albeit with a heavy and distinctive Alabama accent), and love the land of the sun and its people. He would return again and again, finally choosing to live part of each year in a second home there with his beloved wife, Sally. His friendship with Hudson Strode, his legendary writing instructor at the University of Alabama who shared his love for Mexico, only strengthened his ties to the land south of the border.

Wayne began his journalism career at age 15 as part-time sports reporter for his home town *Tuscaloosa News*. After graduation from the University of Alabama, he took his love of writing to Montgomery, ultimately joining the staff of the *Montgomery Journal*, where he began a long writing career. History could hardly have placed him in a better locale at a more important time with so astounding a cast of characters: the Freedom Riders; terrorists who bombed homes and churches; brutal racial murderers; compliant city and state officials; regular Ku Klux Klan and White Citizens Council rallies; Governor George C. Wallace; Rosa Parks; Martin Luther King, Jr.; Ralph David Abernathy; E. D. Nixon; Johnnie Carr; Fred Gray; J. L. Chestnut; Asa Carter; Charles "Chuck" Morgan; Morris Dees; the Selma-to-Montgomery March; Attorney General Bill Baxley's prosecution of the terrorists who bombed 16th Street Baptist Church and murdered four young black girls as they prepared for Youth Day. A longtime U. S. Secretary of State once entitled his memoir, *Present At The Beginning*. Insofar as Wayne's journalistic career was concerned, he could have used the same title because the Movement was in its infancy when he arrived on the scene, and he was able to interview most of its major players.

Covering the Movement was no easy task and involved considerable danger. People of the darkness strike journalists first because they provide the images and narrative that shape public opinion. Destroy the cameras. Tear up the notebooks. Assault the writers. We witnessed it all in Montgomery. And where it succeeds, the forces of light are confused, divided, and impotent. Wayne first encountered the danger as he unlocked his apartment door while investigating establishment involvement in the murder of a young black man. A sudden and severe blow to the back of his head sent him to the hospital with a concussion.

Eleven years of covering Civil Rights as a reporter for the *Journal* and as a stringer for *Time* magazine and the *New York Times* from the epic center of the fight for freedom in America left him exhausted. Part of his personal therapy consisted of a detour into another genre of literature. Blending personal memoir, history, and fiction into a pattern shared by fellow Alabama journalists Howell Raines and Rick Bragg, Wayne told about the world from the interior perspective of a rural Alabama boyhood. His fictional works, *Thunder of Angels*, *The Spider's Web*, *My Heart is in the Earth*, *And Beyond the Night*, bear much the same relationship of fiction to history as his friend Harper Lee's *To Kill A Mockingbird*. As novelist Pat Conroy wrote of *Beyond the Night*: "Wayne Greenhaw writes about Alabama the way Eudora Welty writes about Mississippi, with great passion, authority, and love of the land." Wayne's moral conscience and sense of justice are rarely missing in any of his 22 books. He was, in fact, a fine example of Robert Frost's maxim about good writing: "No tears in the writer, no tears in the reader. No surprise for the writer, no surprise for the reader."

There is adequate validation of his passion and his craft: the applause of fellow writers such as Howell Raines, Rick Bragg, Harper Lee, and Winston Groom; selection as the 2005 recipient of the University of Alabama's Clarence Cason Award; selection for the 2006 Harper Lee Award for the state's distinguished writer; the Hectar Award of the Hall School of Journalism at Troy State University; the Hackney Literary Award from Birmingham-Southern College; induction into Auburn University's Alabama Journalism Hall of Fame (yes, we at Auburn do recognize courage and genius wherever we find it).

Wayne, of course, had a lifelong lover's quarrel with his beloved though deeply conflicted and sometimes infuriating home state. His indictment of it led him gingerly but inexorably into politics, and in 1993-94 he served Governor James E. Folsom, Jr., as State Tourism Director. In the 1980s he edited and published *Alabama* magazine. Early in the twenty-first century he used his chairmanship of the Alabama Humanities Foundation to call us to a celebration of the mind of this state that matched our regard for its athletic eminence. Telling the good stuff about Alabama always did please him more than telling the bad. Stitching together all the complex parts of Wayne's life reminds me of some passages from the Bible that explore a common theme, passages that I suspect he read as a boy during that idealistic time of recovery and renewal:

1st John 1:5-7: *"Here is the message we heard from him and pass on to you: that God is light, and in him there is no darkness at all. If we claim to be sharing in his life while we walk in the dark, our words and our lives are a lie; but if we walk in the light as he himself is in the light, then we share together a common life...."*

Matthew 5:14-16: *"You are the light of the world. A town that stands on a hill cannot be hidden. When a lamp is lit, it is not put under the meal-tub, but on the lamp-stand, where it gives light to everyone in the house. And you, like the lamp, must shed light among your fellows, so that, when they see the good you do, they may give praise to your Father in heaven."*

John 12:35-36: *"Jesus answered them: ' The light is among you still, but not for long. Go on your way while you have the light, so that darkness may not overtake you. He who journeys in the dark does not know where he is going. While you have the light, trust in the light, so that you may become people of light.' And after these words Jesus went away from them into hiding."*

My favorite theologian, Union Seminary Professor Reinhold Niebuhr, wrote two books decades apart in the first half of the twentieth century. Both were born in the ethical dualism of ancient Judaism and Christianity: law/grace; faith/works;

rules/freedom; sin/righteousness; old life/new life; death/resurrection; light/dark. Niebuhr's first book, *Moral Man and Immoral Society*, written early in the century, reflected the author's naive assumption that humans are inherently good and warped only by the injustice of the societies in which they reside. By the early 1940s, he had changed his mind. The rise of Fascism, Nazism, Communism, and other forms of totalitarianism, together with genocide, massive poverty, and ever widening class divisions, moderated his overly optimistic theology. In the second book, entitled *Children of Light and Children of Darkness*, he wrote that despite the best intentions of the people of light, all societies contain malevolent children of darkness who perpetuate themselves by intolerance, injustice, violence, and war.

Wayne was one of those remarkable people who understood the power of darkness without despairing about the capacity of light to overcome it. He constantly challenged us to move from the dark, morose, and fearful vales of our lives to the bright and hopeful uplands of our better natures. During a long session of writing about our irrationality and darkness, he never ceased to believe in our capacity for reason and light.

Now that voice is silent, and we must take whatever comfort we can from Wayne's lifetime of hope. For Sally and all his friends there is assurance in the words of theologian Paul Tillich that: "Grace strikes us when we are in great pain and restlessness . . . sometimes at that moment a wave of light breaks into our darkness, and it is as though a voice were saying, 'You are accepted.'"

Printed with permission from the author.

196

# Literary World Lost a Giant in former AU Prof

by Mary Belk

In the midst of the turbulent 1960s, I was sheltered in the peaceful Loveliest Village on the Plains. While sit-ins and anti-Vietnam War protests turned violent at Kent State and Berkeley, my undergraduate days were calm and untroubled, leaving me with nothing better to do than get an education.

When I gaze back on my time at Auburn, it seems I had more than my fair share of good teachers. One of my great loves back then, as now, was English. I was fortunate to have teachers who instructed and inspired me.

Madison Jones, Auburn University's longtime writer-in-residence, was one of those professors. When I sat in his classroom, he'd written three novels. The first, *The Innocent*, had been reviewed heartily by Robert Penn Warren, and *A Buried Land* had been compared favorably to Dostoyevsky's *Crime and Punishment*. But unlike many scholarly professors, he had a wry sense of humor, and a nice slow way of talking with some gestures of the hands.

He didn't talk about his success as a novelist. Instead, he shared an occasional story about growing up on a farm in Tennessee and his love of horses. He mentioned that he didn't type but wrote on a yellow legal pad with a no. 2 pencil.

After I graduated, Jones' book *An Exile* became famous when it was made into the Hollywood movie "I'll Walk the Line" starring Gregory Peck. But because most of his books were quite literary, he was known as a writer's writer. Some called him the Thomas Hardy of the South. Others have placed his work in the same class as the best writings of Sophocles, Flaubert, Faulkner, Melville, Conrad, and Ibsen.

I moved back to Auburn a bit later in life, and I was looking for ways to increase my writing skills, so I signed up for a fiction-writing class that Jones taught. One night a week he lounged behind his desk and in his deep, raspy voice read our stories aloud. He met with each of us one-on-one in his office several times during the quarter to talk about our writing. When he said he liked my short stories, I mustered up the courage to start submitting fiction for publication.

I was uncommonly sad last week when I saw the obituary marking the passing of my mentor, Madison Jones. As I stood in the foyer reading, I remembered when I was nineteen sitting in his classroom feeling the magic. I think I knew, even then, that having him for a teacher was a gift. And now I just wish I'd told him.

Reprinted with permission from the author.

# The Outline of a Man

## by Rheta Grimsley Johnson

When you are very young, it's hard to appreciate a man's total worth. You know so little about life, about anything, that comprehending a more completed human is nigh impossible.

I considered my Auburn English professor Charlie Rose to be "cool," in the vernacular of that simpler day. That's about all I knew: He was cool. I didn't know then that he loved fencing, classic movies, and jazz piano. I didn't know he was a Russian linguist during the Korean War. I had enough sense, however, to find him interesting. At the time, that was important.

Charlie Rose held office hours in a booth at Jack's hamburger restaurant instead of in the high-rise Haley Center that was institutional and beige. I loved that departure. Charlie—at his insistence, we called him Charlie, not Dr. Rose—made himself available where the coffee was black and hot and the cups big enough to hold a little something extra.

He was an engaging teacher, and the creative writing course for which I had him in the 1970s was over too soon. I may be wrong about this—memory can work tricks—but I don't recall a book assigned for the class. Charlie Rose would read to us, for us, passages from some work that illustrated his point, and we'd listen. Then we wrote. And Charlie Rose reacted. In that way we improved. It was pearls before swine, but he was too fine and kind to consider us swine.

I remember to this day tips he gave me about dialogue. Turns out a lot of dialogue is "understood," and doesn't have to be "expressed." He improved my short stories with a few deft marks of his pen and a quiet suggestion or two. I'd leave that restaurant thinking I might have some kind of future with words, or at least some kind of future. And the ability to give an insecure kid that feeling might be the best definition of teaching that there is.

I learned more about Charlie Rose much later after mentioning in a newspaper column that he and an unforgettable Auburn French professor, Alexander Posniak, were two of my favorite teachers. Charlie Rose responded, with a beautiful letter rife with music references. He played for years in a jazz band, another little something I'd not known.

Mailed along with the letter was an amazing gift—half a dozen paper doll soldiers, elaborately detailed Napoleonic officers Charlie had drawn with pen and ink, then filled in with water color. He had cut them out, mounted them on cardboard, and fitted each with a handmade stand. Turns out he had drawn hundreds of the accurate and armed men, most of which were lost in a house fire.

The last time I saw Charlie Rose was at a party, where he walked in supported by a cane and an adoring cadre of former English students. Life had lobbed a few at Charlie, but somehow he remained undiminished. In the decades since I'd learned from Charlie, he had retired after teaching for thirty-four years, published dozens of short stories in literary quarterlies, written four screenplays, been a Tennessee Williams Scholar at a Sewanee conference, and a Hospice Volunteer of the Year. He wrote a book based on his hospice experience.

In his obituary last week, they said Charlie Rose was entertaining nursing-home residents with his jazz piano until he died there at eighty.

I think it says something about a man if you admire the outline but are still filling in the details when he dies. He was dimensional, like one of his own cardboard soldiers, and the colors that washed the man were vibrant and true.

# Good-bye Cousin Kathryn
## by Harvey H. Jackson

I got back Sunday to the news that Kathryn Tucker Windham had died at home in her beloved Selma.

I can imagine the scene there then, imagine family and friends going out to the back shed and removing the Rose Point Crystal (service for 1twelve, complete with water pitcher and butter dish) from the custom-built pine coffin where she kept it. And I can imagine her being laid to rest in that coffin, according to her wishes.

We called ourselves "cousins," Kathryn and I, though we were cousins only by marriage and even that was stretching it a bit.

Her Uncle Bertie was a hard-working, tight-fisted, no-nonsense man from Thomasville who came down to open a drugstore in Grove Hill, get rich and marry the prettiest girl in town. That was my Great-Aunt MeMe.

Now, you might think that we—Kathryn and I—would celebrate this union and revere his memory, but we knew that our common kin was a hard man to be around, so instead we bonded over the story she told of how, when he died, her mother insisted that she get to the funeral well ahead of the crowd.

"Why so early?" Kathryn asked.

"I want to get a front-row seat to hear if anyone will say anything good about Bertie Tucker."

But we had more going for us than a reprehensible relative.

We had a general love of history and a specific love for a good story.

Although I had known her, or at least of her, most of my life, it was not until I returned to Alabama in 1990 that we really became friends. I was working on a book on Alabama rivers, and since she lived in one of the state's true river towns and had written on the subject, it seemed only natural that I would go visit.

I arrived early. We talked a bit, snacked on graham crackers spread with pimento cheese, clarified family connections, and decried the loss of so many Selma landmarks—especially the old Hotel Albert, the Venetian Palace of a building that once dominated downtown.

Then we loaded up and headed into the Black Belt. "Into the Black Belt"—like we were going into some strange, exotic land from which we might never return. But with Cousin Kathryn we were safe. She knew where to go and who would be there.

Along the way, she did what she did best—told stories that linked us to times past and resurrected people long gone from the earth. She also introduced me to the living, like William Harris, former river rat turned folk artist who ran a store at Possum Bend. He had promised to paint her a picture of a mule and buzzards and she wanted to remind him that she was still waiting for it.

When the day was done, we ate an early supper at Hancock's Barbeque (her favorite).

Then I took her home.

When I left, she gave me a small porcelain room number she had rescued when they tore down the old hotel.

Other visits followed.

More than once I took a class down to see her. I let her set the agenda and it was always different. A trip to Old Cahaba, where we picnicked on the site of Alabama's first capital. A walking tour of Selma's Live Oak Cemetery, where she pointed out graves of little-known people we should know more about.

After she finished one of her stories, a student who was yet to balance skepticism with a sense of whimsy, asked her, "Did that really happen"?

"Well," she said with a faint smile, "if it did not happen that way, it should have."

Those were good times.

There were not enough of them.

Now there won't be any more.

Despite frequent invitations, I never made it to her New Year's Day black-eyed peas and cornbread lunch, when her doors were thrown open to anyone who wanted to make sure luck would follow for another year.

Nor did I do with her so many other things I should have done.

Like take my children by more often.

My son got to know her. My daughter, hardly at all.

Our last communication was the graduation gift she sent the boy. A money clip. The sort a young gentleman should carry, for we all know that pulling out a billfold for minor transactions is, well, tacky.

When it arrived, I recalled a bit of poetry she loved, a verse by Jan Struther. Cousin Kathryn said she wanted it on her tombstone.

"She was twice blessed:

"She was happy:

"She knew it."

That was Cousin Kathryn.

She left out one thing.

We all were blessed by her being here.

I think I'll have some graham crackers and pimento cheese.

# Section IV
# Contributor Bios

# Anne Carroll George

(1927-2001), originally from Montgomery, Alabama, attended Judson College, received a B.A. from Samford University and a M.A. from the University of Alabama. Halfway through her doctorate in English, she realized she did not want to just study other people's writing, wanting instead to do her own writing. It was the best decision she ever made.After marrying and moving to Birmingham, Alabama, George taught in the public school system for some twenty+ years.

She was a co-founder of the literary Druid Press, and a regular contributor to literary and poetry publications.Her first mystery novel was an Agatha Christie Award-winner, and she followed that novel with seven more in the Southern Sisters series. Carroll was the 1994 Alabama State Poet. She was nominated for several awards, including the Pulitzer for a book of verse entitled *Some of It Is True*. George has grandchildren at Auburn and her papers are collected at the Ralph Brown Draughon Library at Auburn University.

## Bibliography

*Dreamer, Dreaming Me*, 1980, Druid Press, Poetry
*Wild Goose Chase*, 1982, Druid Press, Poetry
*Spraying Under the Bed for Wolves*, 1985, Druid Press, Poetry
*Some of It Is True*, 1993, Curbow Publications, Poetry
*This One and Magic Life: A Novel of a Southern Family*, 1999, William Morrow, Fiction
*The Map that Lies Between Us*, 2000, Black Belt Press, Poetry

Southern Sisters Mystery Series:
*Murder on a Girls' Night Out*, Avon, 1996
*Murder on a Bad Hair Day*, Avon, 1996
*Murder Runs in the Family*, Avon, 1997
*Murder Makes Waves*, William Morrow/Avon, 1997
*Murder Gets a Life*, William Morrow/Avon, 1998
*Murder Shoots the Bull*, William Morrow/Avon, 1999
*Murder Carries a Torch*, William Morrow/Avon, 2000
*Murder Boogies with Elvis*, Harper Collins/Avon, 2001

# Olivia Pienezza Solomon

(1937-2007), from Tallassee, Alabama, received B.A. and M.A. degrees in English from The University of Alabama. She taught English and literature at Auburn University and Troy State University.

Her short stories appeared in *Forum* (Ball State University, Muncie, Indiana, 1969 and 1977), *The Carolina Quarterly* (Chapel Hill, NC, 1971), *The Ohio Review* (Ohio University, Athens, 1972), *Roanoke Review* (Roanoke College, Salem, VA, 1972), *Quarterly Review of Literature* (Princeton, NJ, 1972-1973), and *California Quarterly* (University of California-Davis, 1974).

In collaboration with her husband, Jack Payne Solomon, she produced six volumes of Alabama folklore studies. She also wrote poetry and published a collection of children's plays. In her later years, she authored several privately published works of history. *Down Blackjack Road*, a collection of previously published and new stories, became available in 2007.

Solomon's papers are collected at the Ralph Brown Draughon Library at Auburn University.

# Bibliography

*Wild, Wildwood Flower and Other Deep South Tales*, 1979, Portals Press
*Five Folk Comedies*, 1983, Portals Press, 1983, Contemporary versions of classic children's tales
*Letters to the Tallassee Armory*, 1998, Colonial Press, Tallassee, Letters from Col. James Burton, Macon, GA, to Capt. Wm. Bolles and Major J.V. Taylor, Tallassee, Transcribed and edited, with commentary and photographs.
Expanded edition: *The Tallassee Armory: 1864-1865*.
*Down Blackjack Road*, 2007, Lulu Publications, Short stories
*Our Bethel*, 2007, First United Methodist Church of Tallassee, Tallassee, AL, A comprehensive history
*Tukabatchi Sketches*, 2007, Lulu Publications, 2007, The life and times of the Creek Indians, especiallyTukabatchi (Talisi), site of the capitol of the Creek Nation

**Mary Adams Belk** lives in Auburn, Alabama where she writes a weekly column for the *Opelika-Auburn News*. She has published a number of short stories and nonfiction articles. Her short stories have earned awards in the Alabama Writers' Conclave competition and have appeared in such magazines as *Chesapeake Bay* and *Southern Women's Review*.

**Budge Breyer**, a Nashville native born in 1919, received a B.A. degree from Vanderbilt University in 1939, a M.A. from Louisiana State University in 1940, and a PhD. from the University of Virginia in 1948. While at Vanderbilt he was a student of Donald Davidson, a member of the Fugitive/Agrarian literary group, and corresponded with him for many years. He served in the United States Army during World War II. Breyer later became a professor of English at Auburn University, becoming Professor Emeritus of English in September 1985.

**Mary Helen Brown**, a native of Center, Texas, teaches in the Department of Communication and Journalism and is the Breeden Scholar-in-Residence at the Center for the Arts and Humanities at Auburn University. She still loves baseball and regularly practices her spiritual gift of hearing ice cream trucks several blocks away.

**Joseph A. Buckhalt** grew up in Dothan, Alabama, where his parents owned and operated Monarch Dry Cleaners. He is presently Wayne T. Smith Distinguished Professor at Auburn University. He is married to Dr. Mona El-Sheikh, originally from Alexandria, Egypt, and they are parents of two children, Hala and Alex.

**James Buford** is a management consultant who lives and writes in Auburn. In addition to his most recent work, *The House Across the Road*, Jim has published three collections of essays and a social history. As loyal alum he follows the fortunes of Auburn's student athletes on the field of honor, and can often be found enjoying the fare at the Mellow Mushroom, where he recommends their ham and cheese on rye and a Blue Moon on draft with a slice of orange.

Pushcart Prize nominee **Marian Carcache** has published in various journals and anthologies including *Shenandoah, Belles Lettres, Crossroads: Stories of the Southern Literary Fantastic, and Climbing Mt. Cheaha: Emerging Alabama Writers. Under the Arbor*, an opera made from her short story by the same name, premiered in Birmingham and appeared on PBS stations nationwide. *Be The Flame*, a collection of fiction, poetry, and memoir by she and her sisters in The

Mystic Order of East Alabama Fiction Writers, has been weell-received. Marian grew up in rural Russell County, Alabama, and now lives in Auburn.

**Wendy W. Cleveland** taught high school English for thirty years in Ithaca, New York, before moving to Auburn, Alabama, where she has mentored AU student athletes and presently teaches a language class called Say What? for the Christian Women's Job Corps. A member of the Alabama Writers' Forum, she enjoys learning about kudzu, collards, dogtrot houses, and all things Southern.

Formerly a math professor at Auburn University, **Peg Daniels** writes both fiction and creative nonfiction. Her nonfiction has been or will be published in *New Mobility* and *Kaleidoscope*, and her short stories have appeared in *Kaleidoscope, moonShine Review*, and *Southern Women's Review*. One day her mystery novel will be published.

**Mary Dansak** has loved animals and writing all her life. She belongs to a writers' group whose first book, *Be the Flame*, was recently published. As well as writing, Mary is a sixth grade science teacher. She lives in Auburn with her husband and their youngest daughter, and enjoys a kinship to all the local crows to this day.

Poet **Melissa Dickson** is the author of *Cameo* (2011). Her work has appeared in *North American Review, Southern Women's Review, Birmingham Arts Journal*, and *Southern Humanities Review*, among others. She began publishing her work while a student at Auburn in the late 1980s. She holds a B.F.A. from Auburn and M.F.A. from both The School of Visual Arts and Converse College.

**Jeremy M. Downes** is a Professor of English at Auburn University and has recently been named the department head. His most recent scholarly work is *The Female Homer: An Exploration of Women's Epic Poetry.* His third collection of poetry, *Too Small to Read*, is forthcoming from Auburn's New Plains Press.

**Virginia Mitchell Edwards**, a native of West Point, Mississippi, received a B.S. in English Education at Wright State University, Dayton, Ohio, and an M.A. at Auburn University. She taught high school English and journalism in Hurtsboro and Notasulga, Alabama. She was a columnist for *Tuskegee News* and *Daily Times Leader* in her hometown. She and husband, Col. Ollie Edwards, USAF/retired, reside in Auburn. They have three children, five grandchildren, and one great-grandchild.

**Claire Feild** teaches English composition at Southern Union Community College in Opelika, Alabama. She was born and grew up in Yazoo City, Mississippi, the town where the hills meet the Mississippi Delta. She has also taught English in middle school, high school, and university settings, and is a former writing consultant for students in the College of Business at Auburn University. Her most recent poetry book *Mississippi Delta Women in Prism* was published by NewSouth Books in Montgomery, Alabama. A portion of her memoir *A Delta Vigil* was published in *Boston's Full Circle: A Journal of Poetry and Prose*. Her poetry has been published in numerous print literary journals, such as *The Carolina Quarterly; Birmingham Arts Journal; The Chattahoochee Review;* and many others.

Suspense, supernatural, and young adult fiction writer **Stephen Gresham** has been intrigued by the gothic tradition of the South since moving to Auburn in 1975 for a teaching position at Auburn University in the English Department. Gresham studied journalism for two years at Wichita State University, where he began his professional writing career as a freelance sports reporter at the *Wichita Eagle*. He then transferred to Kansas State Teachers College (now Emporia State University) to earn a B.A. and M.A. He completed a PhD. in English Renaissance literature at the University of Missouri. He has published a number of novels and books of short stories. Gresham retired from Auburn University in 2008 and currently resides in Auburn with his wife.

**Carol Hartwig** appreciates her southern roots as an Alabama native, Auburn High 1968. She attended university at Brown and Wisconsin before completing a Master's degree in 1999 at the University of Victoria, British Columbia, Canada. She is a vigorous advocate for the environment and endangered species. The natural world is her refuge and inspiration.

**William Ogden Haynes** is from Opelika, Alabama, and taught at Auburn University for thirty-three years. He has published in *California Quarterly, Quantum Poetry Magazine, Front Porch Review, Full of Crow, Indigo Rising, Forge, Houston Literary Review,* and *PIF* Magazine. His chapbook *Five Thousand Days* has been accepted for publication by Negative Capability Press.

**Peter Huggins** has published three books of poems, *Necessary Acts, Blue Angels*, and *Hard Facts*; in addition, he is the author of a picture book, *Trosclair* *and the Alligator,* which has appeared on the PBS show Between the Lions, and a novel for younger readers, *In the Company of Owls.*

**Bailey Jones** splits his time between his home in Opelika, Alabama, and his Lake Martin home. He graduated from Auburn University having studied both Wildlife and English and has penned a book of memories entitled *Growing Up: Tales About Life on the Lake.* Bailey and his wife, Allyson Comstock, are the driving force behind the non-profit Sundilla Acoustic Concert Series.

**Madison Jones**, born in Nashville, Tennessee, was the son of a Presbyterian businessman, and spent his early years living in suburban Nashville. At age fourteen, his father purchased Sycamore Farm in hill country twenty-five miles north of the city. At seventeen, Jones dropped out of Vanderbilt University to become a farmer, moving to Sycamore Farm where he lived for a year and a half. He became associated with the Southern Agrarians, which proved a great influence on his later work. After graduating from Vanderbilt in 1949 and getting a M.A. at the University of Florida he taught English at the University of Tennessee before accepting a creative writing position at Auburn University in 1956. He retired from Auburn in 1987, having been a longtime writer in residence. He was the author of eleven novels: *The Innocent* (1957), *Forest of the Night* (1960), *A Buried Land (Sometimes I Walk the Line)* (1963), *An Exile* (1967), *A Cry of Absence* (1971), *Passage Through Gehenna* (1978), *Season of the Strangler* (1982), *Last Things* (1989), *To the Winds* (1996), *Nashville 1864: The Dying of the Light* (1997), and *The Adventures of Douglas Bragg* (2008).

**Gail Langley** grew up in the shadow of Alabama Polytechnic Institute. She is a third generation Auburn graduate. She still lives near the college with her husband Bob, who is a saint, and her son, Rivers, who isn't. Gail, along with her writing guild, The Mystic Order of East Alabama Fiction Writers, recently published *Be the Flame*, a collection of short stories.

Having been a high school English teacher in Iowa for thirteen years and a professor of English Education at Auburn University for twenty-seven, **Terry Ley** has enjoyed an extended busman's holiday since his retirement: teaching a memoir-writing class for the Osher Lifelong Learning Institute (OLLI) at Auburn University for the past nine years.

**Lan Lipscomb** was born in Lee County Hospital, raised in Auburn, and graduated from Auburn University in English in 1979. After thirteen years of graduate school and of being blown about by the academic trade winds, he returned to Auburn in 1994 to make his home and raise his children. He's a professor of English at Troy University, Montgomery Campus, specializing in medieval and Renaissance literature, but he has been interested in Alabama history for the past ten years and enjoys researching in archives. He's married to Stacy and has two sons, Mark (who just graduated from Auburn) and Sam, and a stepdaughter Jonah.

**Taylor Littleton** was a professor of English and Vice President of Academic Affairs at Auburn University. He attended Florida State University where he received a B.A., M.A., and PhD. in English Literature. He served in the Korean War and in 1957 began teaching at Auburn University. In 1960, he became an assistant professor and became chair of the English Department in 1961. In 1972, then Auburn University President Dr. Philpott appointed Littleton Vice President for Academic Affairs, where he served for ten and one-half years. Littleton continued his career at the University as the Franklin Foundation professor after his formal retirement. He now provides instruction at any number of OLLI classes in Auburn.

**Janet Mauney** has previously published short stories in the *Apalachee Review*, *Woodrider*, *The Southeast Review*, *Q Magazine*, *Belles' Letters*, and *Climbing Mount Cheaha*, as well as many reviews and articles about art exhibits in *Art Papers*. She currently teaches writing and literature at Auburn University in Auburn, Alabama.

**Dottie McKissick** graduated in Elementary and Early Childhood Education from Auburn University and taught kindergarten and first grade. She married and had three children who are all now grown. Retired, she has had the opportunity to explore a life-long interest in writing, and writes poetry, memoir, and short fiction. As a member of OLLI, she had the opportunity to study the craft of poetry writing under Mary Carol Moran for two years and memoir writing in the OLLI class "Writing Our Lives" led by Terry Ley. In addition, she audited AU English Department's course the "Poetry Writing Workshop" class under both Natasha Trethewey in the 1990s and Jeremy Downes this past year.

**Jessica Nelson** grew up in south Georgia where she ran around barefoot and read indiscriminately. "Dirt Road" is her first published story, and is a cocktail of family history, memory, and invention.

**Judith Nunn** grew up in Methodist parsonages across south Alabama and northwest Florida. After graduating magna cum laude from Huntingdon College, where she was the first recipient of the Thompson Award for Creative Writing and editor of the literary magazine, she came to Auburn University on an English fellowship, married a local cotton farmer, and moved down Wire Road to Beehive to begin a family. When the youngest of her three children was in pre-school, Judy began proof-reading part-time at a local newspaper, and was soon writing feature stories, columns, and news and winning press association awards. After ten years of journalism, she stopped writing altogether, until The Mystic Order of East Alabama Fiction Writers inspired her to return to fiction.

**Charlene Redick** is a playwright, novelist, poet, essayist and painter. Her plays have been produced all over the world, nominated for the Susan Blackburn Prize and won the Dayton Future Fest Prize and the American Express/Fund for New Plays/Kennedy Center Award. She won the Coffee House verse competition at Huntingdon College, Montgomery, Alabama. She was a finalist or semi-finalist in many playwriting and fiction writing competitions; won third place in The Hackney Award Competition at Birmingham Southern College-Writing Today Festival; and enjoyed a staged reading of her play, *A Sonnet for Sarajevo* at the Alabama Shakespeare Festival's Southern Writers Project. She is the recipient of two writing grants from the Alabama Council of the Arts, and the Kathryn Woodruff Scholarship in Fiction Writing from the University of Tennessee in Knoxville. She has taught playwriting at Auburn University/Montgomery and many fiction writing and screenwriting workshops

**Charles Rose** (Charlie) taught English at Auburn University for thirty-four years. A native of Indiana, he held degrees from Vanderbilt and the University of Florida and published many short stories and articles. He was a past Hospice Volunteer of the Year and in 2004 was awarded an Alabama State Council on the Arts Fellowship for literary arts/fiction. From his experience as a hospice worker, Rose authored *In the Midst of Life: A Hospice Volunteer's Story*. He died in 2011 shortly before the publication of *A Ford in the River, A Collection of Short Stories*, from NewSouth Books.

**Bob Sanders** is storyteller, writer, and fifty-three-year veteran radio personality of Auburn's WAUD. He has previously published a memoir entitled *Friends, Family and Frontier Country: Growing Up in West Alabama.*

**Helen Silverstein**, co-editor of *Southern Women's Review*, writes fiction, nonfiction, and poetry. She publishes in journals as diverse as *OBIT* magazine and *Big Pulp*. Helen has a B.A. from Bowdoin College and a M.A. from the University of Wisconsin-Madison.

**Jennifer Soule** holds an M.F.A. in Creative Writing from the University of Nebraska. Her poems have appeared in *South Dakota Review, The Sow's Ear Poetry Review, Birmingham Poetry Review, North Dakota Quarterly,* and *Modern Haiku*, among others. She has been a community organizer, clinical social worker, and professor in various parts of the country.

**Peggy A. Stelpflug**, retired English teacher, enjoys visiting with her children and grandchildren, painting, reading, and taking classes. She is the author of *Home of the Infantry: A History of Fort Benning.* Her poem "Old Men" is dedicated to her husband Bill, who for fifty-six years was her friend, lover, and companion.

**Kyes Stevens** is the founder of the Alabama Prison Arts + Education Project at Auburn University. She has presented at many national and international conferences and symposia about APAEP. She earned her M.A. in Women's History and M.F.A. in poetry from Sarah Lawrence College in New York. She is a practicing poet who was awarded a grant from the National Endowment for the Arts and the Department of Justice to teach poetry at the Talladega Federal Prison in 2001. She has published poetry in the *Blue Collar Review, CrossRoads: A Southern Journal of Culture*, on *poetrysoutheast.com*, and in the *Southern Women's Review*, among others. She served on the Waverly, Alabama Town Council from 2003-08, was a volunteer firefighter in Waverly for eleven years, and still resides in the small Alabama town.

**Oxford Stroud**, a native Alabamian, spent most of his life in the state of his birth. His local reputation as a superb raconteur and writer was realized more widely when at age sixty-seven, eight years after his retirement from the English Department at Auburn University, his novel *Marbles* was published by a major national publisher. For the latter part of World War II, Stroud served with the U.S. Eighth Army Air Force in England. After the Pacific war ended, he enrolled in a special informal course on English literature at Oxford University. After returning to the states, he first attended Southwestern Presbyterian University in Clarksville, Tennessee, but soon transferred to Alabama Polytechnic Institute. There, he earned a B.S. in English Education in 1949. He and Mary Anne Porter were married in 1950 and had three sons and two daughters. Stroud was awarded a M.A. in English, also from API, in 1953. After having worked for the Alabama Department of Public Welfare in Wilcox County for a year, Stroud joined the faculty of the English Department of API. Teaching there for the next thirty years, he made his advanced composition classes a popular class among the students. He retired in 1983. Stroud died in Auburn on March 12, 2002, after battling melanoma, and is buried in Camden, Wilcox County. His second novel, *To Yield a Dream*, was published posthumously. He was working on a sequel to *Marbles* at the time of his death.

**Johnny Summerfield** has a B.A. in English from Florida and a M.F.A. in Writing from Goddard. He is an Assistant Professor of Basic Writing at Columbus State University. He is publisher/chief editor of Summerfield Publishing/New Plains Press. He is a co-author of *Remembering Sicily or Ricordando la Sicilia* from Legas Pubs., New York and Toronto, as well as a co-author of a still untitled experimental novel in verse, to be published by Negative Capability Press. His chapbook *I, Suwannee* is currently being re-realized and will become *I Suwannee with Poems and Stories* in the near future. Johnny has nearly finished his novel titled *Naxos*, which he has labored over for the last two years. He has taught and attended many workshops on writing and plans on teaching more in the future.

**Amber Tidwell** is currently living in Hangzhou, China, for a year where she is teaching college English and indulging her wanderlust. She earned her B.S. from Troy University, her M.Div. from New Orleans Baptist Theological Seminary, and her M.F.A. in Creative Writing from California State University, Fresno, California. She was an Opelika resident and taught English at Columbus Technical College while moonlighting as a barista at Starbucks. She has also been published with the *interrobang?!*, an online magazine focused on finding creativity, truth, debate, comedy, and great questions.

**Christy Truitt** is a feature writer and copy editor for *East Alabama Living* magazine and director of Network Creative Media, an advertising agency. The Demopolis, Alabama, native is an on-air talent for radio and television commercials and web promos. Christy is on the advisory board of the Sigma Lambda Chapter of Kappa Delta sorority and a Sunday school volunteer. A graduate of Auburn University, Christy lives in Auburn, Alabama, with her husband and three children. Hobbies include annoying each of them as much as possible.

**Peggy Walls** enjoys writing poetry and nonfiction. Her poems have been published in various journals and in the chapbook *Reflections on Nature*. Her nonfiction writing has been published in *The Alabama Review* and cited in professional studies. She co-authored *Alexander City* (Arcadia Publishing, 2011).

**Barbara Wiedemann**, professor of English and Director of Creative Writing at Auburn University Montgomery, is the author of two poetry chapbooks, *Half-Life of Love* (2008) and *Sometime in October* (2010), both published by Finishing Line Press. In addition, her poems have appeared in *Kaleidoscope, Blueline, Kerf, Feminist Studies, Paper Street, Acorn,* and other journals.

**Scott Wilkerson**, poet, theorist, and Opelika native, teaches at Columbus State University. He holds a B.A. from Auburn University, an M.L.A. from Auburn-Montgomery, and an M.F.A. from Queens University of Charlotte. His books *Threading Stone* (2009) and the forthcoming *Ars Minotaurica* (2012) are both published by New Plains Press.

**John Williams** teaches at LaGrange College in LaGrange, Georgia. His novel *Lake Moon* was published by Mercer University Press in 2002; he was named Georgia Author of the Year for First Novel that year. With composer Ken Clark he has written five stage musicals. Two of them, *The Kelly's Truck Stop Bop* and *Get It Off Me* have had multiple productions in the area. In 2009 his one-act play *Fish Hungry* won first place in the Society of Southwestern Authors Playwriting competition in Tucson. A single parent, he lives in LaGrange with his son and daughter.

# Section V
# Acknowledgements

Buford, Jim: "Conversation With a Crow" was previously published in *Pie in The Sky* by River City Publishing.

Daniels, Peg: "My Sister, A Girl" was published in a different version in the *Southern Womens' Review*.

Dickson, Melissa: "Parked Under a Crepe Myrtle at the Public Library" first appeared in *Cameo* from New Plains Press. "Robin Lake" appeared in an earlier draft entitled "The Fish" in *Sense Magazine*.

Downes, Jeremy: "Amabala" was previously published in The Peconic Gallery's Hope exhibition in Riverhead, New York, and in *Lost Atlas of Desire* by BlazeVOX [books].

Feild, Claire: "Brickyard Hill" was previously published in *Mississippi Delta Women in Prism* by NewSouth Books.

George, Anne Carroll: "Autumn Apples," "The Grist Mill," "Josie-in-the-Morning," "My Grandmother's Story," "Quilting," and "Turned Funny" were previously published in *The Map That Lies Between Us: New and Collected Poems, 1980-2000* by River City Publishing.

Haynes, William Ogden Haynes: "Dirty Laundry" was previously published in *Front Porch Review*.

Jones, Bailey: "At the End of the Road a Graveyard" was previously published in *Growing Up: Tales About Life on the Lake*.

Jones, Madison: *A Cry of Absence* was previously published by Lousiaiana State University Press.

Littleton, Taylor: "The Greeting Was Always 'Christmas Gift'" was previously published in the *Auburn Villager*.

Mauney, Janet: "Letting in the Light" was previously published under the title "Tornado Lady" in the *Apalachee Review*.

Rose, Charlie: "Mr. Hardcastle" was previously published in *A Ford in The River* by NewSouth Books.

Sanders, Bob: "Fred The Hired Hand" was previously published in *Friends, Family and Frontier Country: Growing Up in West Alabama* by Gnu's Room, Inc.

Silverstein, Helen: "Dandelion Wishes" was previously published by *Haruah: Breath of Heaven*, and on line at *www.haruah.com*

Stelpflug, Peggy: "Old Men" was previously published in *The LLI Review—The Annual Journal of the Osher Lifelong Learning Institute*.

Solomon, Olivia: "The Prophetess" was previously published in *Wild, Wildwood Flower* by Portals Press.

Stroud, Oxford: "Henry" was previously published in *The Auburn Review*.

Solomon & George Publishers would like to thank Bert Hitchcock who cheerfully volunteered to edit this inaugral publication.

A huge thanks to all of the volunteers who contributed in ways great and small to get the manuscript into print.

Special thanks go to Rachel Rimes and John Crenshaw for their assistance in setting up the text, and to John for the cover design.

Thanks also to June Corley for allowing the use of her "WUUP Bird" for the back cover.

We would also like to recognize the support and cooperation of the Solomon and George families in regard to this project. Sadly, Jack Solomon, husband to Olivia and father to Jackie, Suzannah, and Will, passed away before he could see the finished product.

Jack Solomon was raised in Luverne, Alabama. His undergraduate degree was from Troy Teachers' College, his M.A. from Columbia University and his Ed.S. from Peabody College, now a part of Vanderbilt University. Jack taught at Auburn University, Troy State University, and Alexander City State Junior College, now known as Central Alabama Community College. He taught English, drama, and folklore. From 1995 to 2009, he published six books of his own and co-published seven books with Olivia.

## Books by Jack Payne Solomon & Olivia Pienezza Solomon

*Cracklin' Bread and Asfidity.* University of Alabama Press, 1979. Folk recipes and remedies.

*Zachary Zan.* University of Alabama Press. 1979. Children's games, songs, jump rope rhymes, and other lore.

*Ghosts and Goosebumps.* University of Alabama Press. 1981. Ghost tales, tall tales, and superstitions.

*Sweet Bunch of Daisies.* Colonial Press. 1991. Folk songs from Alabama contributors, various musical notation by Sarah Scott.

*Honey in the Rock.* Mercer University Press. 1991. Songs Collected in Sumter County, Alabama, by Ruby Pickens Tartt for the WPA Writers' Project, edited with commentary.

*Gone Home: Southern Folk Gravestone Art.* NewSouth Books. 2004. Collection of 100 sample epitaphs from central Alabama rendered in hand script; with extensive commentary; photographs by Suzannah Solomon Wilson.

*Our Bethel.* A history of the First United Methodist Church of Tallassee. Published by the church. 2007.